I Wrote This SONG

Dayne Avery

I Wrote This Song

iwrotethissong.net

Copyright © 2004 by Dayne Avery

LIBRARY OF CONGRESS REGISTRATION INFORMATION
Registration number Txu1-187-065

ISBN 0-9761323-0-3

Cover design by
Dayne Avery

PUBLISHERS NOTE

--This book is dedicated to every individual strong enough to take the road less traveled on life's journey. Thank you for keeping me company.

1

Without even the slightest warning, the remnants of my peaceful rest were slashed into jagged little pieces, leaving me suddenly awakened into a terrible nightmare.

Hot flashes of pain cloaked my body so intensely they seemed to surge through and sting my flesh from the outer layers of my skin all the way down to my very bones.

"Wake up you GOTDAMNED FAGGOT!"

Those most cutting of words uttered with the most noxious intent reverberated in my eardrums, as I was further jolted from what had been a serene slumber.

The clock's hands up on my bedroom wall read eleven o'clock and those hands of time, all at once became the only things still in the room. *My* hands were now trembling and his were charging toward my body.

Lying down, asleep in my bed, just like I usually was at this time any other evening, only this would prove to be far from a normal night.

I was disoriented for a few moments before realizing what was happening. I knew it couldn't have been just a bad dream, since pain like this had never been present in any of my dreams, especially not this type of deep stinging and burning.

Quickly, I became conscious of the fact that I was being beaten repeatedly in fast, whip-like lashes with a thick, black leather belt.

Lifting me up from my bed with a tight grasp and with the strength of a man twice his size, he yanked me up effortlessly, then threw my body down on the floor in a seamless motion.

"Get up! Get the fuck up right now!" he demanded in a tone that sounded like it could have been the voice of Satan. "What did I do?" I asked. There was no answer. "What did I do?!" I asked again in terror, but still there was no answer.

Panic-stricken, my frozen body would not respond to his raging commands. This only further infuriated the beast he had become.

He grabbed me by my left ankle with an ironclad grip. Soon, I started to feel parts of my body burning again.

Excruciating heat moved across each part of me, as I was now being dragged across the carpet. My mouth opened wide to yell out for help, but no sound came out. Who would I cry out to?

My first instinct was to call out his name as I had before in past times of danger, when I would simply call and wait for him to make everything all right. But this time was different. The same man who I looked to for protection was the man who had suddenly and without warning turned on me.

Instead of my refuge, a savage beast stood possessed by a carnal rage that was trying to beat the life out of me.

"MAMA!!!" I yelled and began to kick my free leg wildly in an attempt to win back the captured ankle. Since he continued to pull, my aggressive thrashing only added to the fiery heat of the rug's burns.

He proceeded to drag my body down the stairs of our home and into the basement. Once there, he slammed the door and ordered me to "Shut up!"

Reality sunk in. I was now deeply in fear for my life. Tears accumulated in my eyes, but I tried my best not to let them fall. Never before had I been in so much fear or in so much pain. Never before had I seen my father so upset, let alone upset with me.

"Faggot!" he yelled over and over again, prompting me to triple-guess his seedy motive. I had never told a single soul the questions I had about my sexuality. Why was he insulting me so? Did he know something about me that I didn't know he knew, or was he just assuming? And if so, was his assumption enough fuel to light this all-consuming fire?

"Get up! Get up, and fight like real men do!" he demanded.

Trying hard to obey, I slowly rose to my feet. Seconds later, he propelled himself toward me and wrapped his large hands around my neck, squeezing until I could no longer breathe. Desperately gasping for air, I shook my head from side to side. I could feel the blood and pressure building in my head as he continued suffocating me.

"How could you?!" he shouted repeatedly.

How could I do what? I wondered. He still had not told me why I was in so much trouble. For the life of me, I could not think of what I had done to piss him off to this brutal extent.

Unwillingly thrust into this tumultuous clash which I was clearly losing on all counts, there was no other alternative now but to defend myself.

With a balled fist and all the strength that I could muster, I drew my arm backward slightly, and then released it with surprising force, striking my father dead center in his nose. Crack! My fist hit his face, startling him. I guess he wasn't prepared for me to actually fight back or hit him so hard since he fell back for a moment before composing himself. With him temporarily knocked off guard, I was also able to remove his grasp from around my neck.

Following a deep inhale, I started coughing uncontrollably, as my lungs attempted to make up for the temporary loss of oxygen.

Meanwhile, I scanned the room looking for something to use as a weapon. He was bigger and stronger, and I was no match for him. I bolted for a shiny red and silver bat lying on the ground a few feet away. It was the same bat that I'd seen him play softball with about a hundred times. Just before reaching it, I felt my body being snatched back by his might. Now, once again I was at his mercy, and his strong hold assured that I would not escape again.

Tears came streaming down my face like raindrops from a mighty storm cloud. I could no longer hold them. Even though I knew by crying I was admitting defeat and giving him the twisted satisfaction of knowing that he'd gotten the best of me, at that point, it really didn't matter.

Never would I have imagined that our relationship would come to this. The man I had loved and felt throughout my entire childhood that I needed just as much as the air I now breathed after a near suffocation was standing over me, throwing blows like I was his archenemy.

I wasn't crying because of the pain from the physical hits, for my body had gone numb, impervious to the torture. I was filled with so much anger and adrenaline that I could only feel sadness and rage. The tears were the result of finally reaching my boiling point. All the frustration, intimidation, insecurities and mental anguish he inflicted had finally gotten the best of me.

Enough was enough and I realized this wasn't right, he wasn't right. As I turned around to face my attacker, something took control of me for the first time that evening.

Something in me ignited, and I just started throwing wild punches, one after the other, not caring how much I was hurting him or how much he may hurt me. I couldn't see anything but his angry eyes locked on me as I tried my best to overpower him. While throwing punches at him, he returned every one with the same strength in which mine had been delivered.

Moments later, we were both on the ground, wrestling, kicking, punching and going at each other with the unleashed rage of two angry pit bulls.

It was hard to believe that this was the same man who had taught me to always do right by people. "Son," he would say, "if you physically hurt someone, in time, their wounds will heal. However, if you kill someone's spirit, that spirit is never as easy to mend." I guessed he had forgotten all about those words of wisdom as he single-handedly succeeded in breaking my spirit that night.

The nastiest hurt had come from seeing the anger and disappointment while he looked me in the eyes and called me a 'faggot'. Everything else from that moment on was painless. The beating only added injury to insult.

Time stilled as the world fell in slow motion, making each second last for what felt like minutes, and each minute span hours.

"Stop it." I heard my mother calmly speak as if she had been watching something that was the norm, like what she was witnessing was just the two of us play-fighting. Couldn't she see that I was in serious trouble? Couldn't she see the blood coming from my head as he repeatedly slammed it against the cold gray concrete floor? Couldn't she see how effortlessly he did this, as if I were nothing but a small rag doll? Did she not hear my desperate pleas for help?

"Jonathan, that's enough! You're hurting him!" she said, slightly more sternly this time. Only then did he release his grip, as the battle neared its resolution. But not before one last powerful knock.

The pain from that last hit was deliberately sent with much more momentum than the rest. It was meant to do much more damage and leave memories of that moment tattooed in my mind. That punch was for all the times my father never got to see me bring a girl to our house before escorting her on a date. It was for never scoring a touchdown on a football team, never shooting a winning jump shot on a basketball team, and for never getting to be the proud parent watching from the sidelines as I hit a homerun and came sliding into home plate in a cloud of dust. It was for the un-known shame I'd caused him because I hadn't inherited his athletic prowess or his charming way with females. It was for the embarrass-ment I'd brought because I would rather draw, sing and do other artistic things than play sports. That hit was for everything I'd done wrong my whole life. It was for not amounting to the son he had always dreamed I would one day become.

He was successful in his attempt to leave a lasting mark. As he reared back his fist and struck my face, hitting me in the mouth, my lip instantly burst wide open by the vigor of his hand. Blood oozed down my face and trickled into a spot where a puddle of warm crimson liquid collected on the cold concrete.

And then it was over.

"Now get your sissy ass from off the floor. Go outside and get in the car. I'll be there in a minute and you better be there," he said, in between heavy panting.

The fight had taken its toll and it was almost impossible to regain my composure after almost being ushered into death by my father's hands. The tears were still falling hard as I pulled myself up from the basement floor, stood up, bowed my head and began to walk up the same staircase that I had been dragged down moments before. I noticed traces of my blood on the carpet. With each step, the numbness subsided until I started to feel pain again. Each step felt like a punch. Each time I closed my eyes I could still hear all the painful taunts from my father. "Faggot" and "sissy" echoed in my head with a painful resonance that was even louder than the ringing in my ears.

I slowly made my journey to the car.

That had to be the longest car ride of my life, all the while wondering where he was taking me and if I would return. We sat in the car perfectly silent, with no radio -- no sound at all except the car on the open road on a night that seemed as dark and melancholy as the mood that embraced me.

The sound of tires skidding across black asphalt and smell of burning rubber stole my attention from my sadness. Under my father's control, the car was steered to the side of the road. As he slammed on the brakes, bringing the car to an abrupt stop, he pounded his fists on the steering wheel so hard I thought it would break just like his voice.

"GET OUT!"

Before exiting, I looked in his eyes and for the first time that night he appeared to be showing an emotion other than fury. It seemed unbelievable, but the once stoic and enraged man was now crying.

"GET OUT!" he shouted again. I followed his command, wondering what else he was going to do to me and if my body could take any more. I looked around at the surroundings of night, at the trees and the moon, thinking how everything looked so peaceful and wondered why I couldn't have that same peace.

As his car door slammed, I turned and watched him go to the trunk, open it, then pull out the same red-and-silver bat I had tried to use on him earlier that night.

"Remember this?" he asked, marching closer toward me. "I'm going to make you never want to even look at another man."

I wanted to run, but knew he would catch me. I wanted to kill him, but I had no fight left. What else could I do but let him have his way and hope everything would be over soon.

Before he had finished talking, he pinned me on the ground and ripped off my sweatpants. My naked lower half was fully exposed to the night air. He rose and with one foot placed on my back so I couldn't escape, started to pound the bat's cold aluminum on my flesh. He beat me over and over again, trying his hardest to force the bat inside of me. My anguished yells echoed down the open road, drifting off into the night.

The next thing I remember was the glaring light from a bright red sign that read "EMERGENCY" as we pulled into the parking lot of Pennsylvania's Daughters of Mercy Hospital.

I thought for a moment about why he had brought me there. Could my father still care about me and had brought me to the hospital to receive medical attention? Never was I so wrong.

He stood there silently eying the emergency sign with a cold, distant stare. A few minutes later, his voice sliced through the silence and wonderings in my mind.

"If you think what I did to you tonight was bad, just let me find out about you so much as even thinking about another man the wrong way and this is just where I will put you! Whether it's by me whooping your ass again, or me having you committed to the psychiatric ward to have your damn head examined. No son of mine will ever be a damn faggot! Do you understand?!" he shouted.

He started the ignition to the car and sped off without waiting for a response.

Our journey came full circle, and we arrived back at the same place where things had gone wrong just hours before as my father placed the car in park. As the car stopped, it was as if someone had fired a starting, pistol sending my feet moving at a hurried pace. I ran as fast as I could back into the house, straight to the bathroom, shutting the door and locking it behind me. Just in case there was a round two lurking on the other side of the door, there would be a slight barrier of protection. He would have to break that door down in order to get to me again.

I wept as I stared in the mirror, wishing for everything to be the way it had been the day before. I looked like a badly shattered version of my former self, covered in rug burns, bruises, scabs, scrapes and scars. My face was all bloody, my lip was terribly busted, and my left eye was swollen shut and turning black. My clothes were dirty and completely tattered. The only thing worse than my outer appearance was the way I felt inside.

"Mirror, mirror on the wall, who in turmoil can I call?" I whispered, while staring at my ghastly reflection.

I wanted to take a bath, but cringed at the very thought of the water meeting my open wounds. Then I thought about lying down to go back to sleep and resting until the pain subsided, but even that seemed too painful. I was in such bad shape that I didn't want to move. My body hurt too much to do anything except stand still and cry, using the tears to try and soothe my overwhelming pain.

What I wanted most of all was for someone to come comfort me, nurse all my hurts and tell me everything was going to be okay. But no one came to comfort me; no one came to my rescue. No one even came to check on me.

I stood in that same spot, frozen, staring into the mirror for hours until my body could no longer stand on its own. The room became black around me as I, still in excruciating pain, passed out on the bathroom floor.

A loud knock on the door woke me. I just lay there, thinking I was dead until I heard my mother's voice telling me to hurry up and get moving so that I would not be late for school. She couldn't be serious! Clearly, I was in no condition to go anywhere. Did she really expect me to go to school after what I had experienced?

When I finally emerged from my refuge, my mother was standing there waiting for me. She looked horrified, but didn't say a word, nor did I say anything to her. Everything we felt in that moment couldn't be expressed so it was pointless to try.

A long silence followed.

While we stood watching each other with sad, eyes, tears began to mount again. Along with the tears came this unstoppable feeling of sorrow as I stood wondering if both my parents had turned against me. Could a parents love die? The uncertainty left me devastated.

It turned out that my mother was serious about me going to school. It seemed everything I had been through came second to my education.

Even though I thought my eyes were all out of tears, they were not. I ended up crying the majority of the day. Each time someone stopped to stare at my black eye and bruises, ask what happened to me, or if I was okay, I would just break down all over again. Whenever I tried to explain to people what happened, all I could do was mouth the words. No sound escaped my lips. The mental and emotional anguish that I felt would not let me vocalize what I had endured. The tears were the only way to describe my torment; that would last for weeks until I was finally strong enough to start the healing process. Long after the physical scars had healed, the emotional healing was only beginning.

   I winced, rigid with fear as I felt myself being awakened and brought back to reality. This is how it all started. Was it happening again? Was I about to be subjected to the same torture a second time?

   After a few moments, I'd realized it was all a dream. The step-by-step reenactment of the fight with my father wasn't real, at least not this time. It was only a bad trip down memory lane.

   Looking back and remembering the details of that night--after years of trying to completely block it from my memory--I thought about how funny the mind is, the things it holds onto versus what it will allow you to let go. Just when I thought I had erased that episode from my memory, it came back to me, I relived that night with all of the same pain and emotion.

   My boyfriend's hand was gently placed on my shoulder and his eyes watched me intensely trying to surmise what was wrong. As our eyes met, he saw the fear trapped in my eyes and helplessly watched while I lay in a puddle of sweat. I was still somewhat disoriented, with a heart racing faster than my thoughts.

   I inhaled deeply, trying hard to forget about the nightmare.

   Some people say they fell in love at first sight. This leads me to believe that it can take only a split second to fall in love. Maybe I didn't fall in love with my soul mate at first sight, but in that second when I looked into his comforting eyes feeling complete and safe, I knew. I do believe that was the moment I fell in love. That moment when I looked in his eyes and felt the soothing warmth of his touch, knowing that his concern was genuine as he wiped away every tear, I felt like I was being introduced to what real love was supposed to be. It was nothing like the sad imitations of love I had known, filled with terms, conditions, boundaries, and always unreliable. That night there was a feeling for this man that seemed different and I realized he was *The One*, the one I had subconsciously been seeking.

2

Gradually, the pungent aroma of magnolia blossoms filled the confines of my 1993 Toyota Camry. My dry eyes read, "Georgia welcomes you!" on a colorful highway sign that fading further into the distance.

With the car windows rolled all the way down and hot wind blowing across me, a zombie-like state that had captured me about 200 miles back continued to hold me captive. This disorientation was a result of my current road trip to Atlanta, a drive that seemed like it would never end.

It was the summer of 1998 and I was soon to begin my first day of college as a freshman at Clark Atlanta University. I was so proud of all my accomplishments and at the fact that I had been able to prosper in spite of a troubled home life that almost broke me in two. My senior year of high school could have made even the toughest man falter. I'd endured things that most would never even have to imagine.

Though life in Pennsylvania had left a permanent bad taste lingering in my mouth, there was still a slight, bittersweet emotion that came over me as I drove and realized I was moving on. I was excited to be getting on with my life, but slightly nervous about what that new life would bring.

The drama at home behind me, I focused on the road ahead, determined to succeed. I drove slowly through campus with the smile of a man sitting on top of the world, ready to take on the task of college life, prove the naysayers wrong, and make everyone who cared proud.

As I arrived at my final destination, I couldn't help but notice my excitement turning into anxiety. Terror lurked, and though I tried to hide my fear behind feigned ambition, it was starting to show. After just turning nineteen and just graduating high school, there I was, thrust into a totally new environment. This was the first time I would be away from home for more than a two-week period and the first time I had ever been in another state alone. I was in a new city where I didn't know a single soul.

Culture shock hit me as I parked my car in front of what was to be my new home– the Clark Atlanta dorms. The dated-looking brick buildings were kind of homey, yet uninviting. Shabby and run down, they made me wonder why the school charged so much for room and board. This was said to be one of the best historically black colleges in the nation, which was why I chose Clark over a handful of other colleges. Hopefully, the state of the dorms would not be a direct reflection on anything else that Clark had to offer. If not, I would be in for a very rude awakening. Nevertheless, I decided to suck it up and remain positive. Like it or not, this was now "home" for me.

Sitting on the devil's lap in the midst of two hells couldn't paint a vivid enough picture of how hot it was in Georgia that day. As I stepped out of the car, an instant sweat popped from every pore on my body, drenching my clothes with moisture. Being from the north, heat like that was foreign to me. In Pennsylvania the only time it got that hot would be during a heat wave, and those only came around every blue moon. It felt like modern day torture and became difficult to breathe in the hot, sticky air around me. While adjusting to the new and unfamiliar climate, I kept chanting, "Stay positive." My goal was not to let anything deter me from having a positive college experience, especially not my first day on campus.

After gathering as many bags as my arms could carry from the trunk of my car, beads of sweat continued to accumulate on my brow, then made their way down my face while I struggled to make my way closer to the dormitory.

"Aye folk, you got olla that, or you need sum help?" a voice from behind me said.

"Huh?" I asked.

I turned around, wondering who was talking to me and trying to piece together as much as I could from the thick, Southern drawl.
"Need sum help, folk?"

The first thing I saw was a row full of beautiful, white teeth greeting me with the brightest, most perfect smile in existence.

Giving the man standing before me a smile and a quick look, I then cut my eyes out into space so that it wouldn't appear as if I was staring too hard at him or his intriguing smile.

During the quick once-over, I noticed that he was about 5'9, weighed about a 160 pounds, and was blessed with a medium "country boy frame." That meant he was thick in all the right places, like he was raised on Southern food and milk. He was very attractive, with smooth, ebony skin and long, jet-black hair that was braided in cornrows, coming down just slightly past his shoulders. He wore blue jean shorts, brand new, un-scuffed white Nike sneakers and a white A-shirt, which we called "wife beaters". His white top exposed a set of solid, muscular arms and a glimpse of a very well defined chest.

"Nah, I got this right here. But I do have some more stuff in the car you can help me with if you want," I said.

At the time I was still looking out into space and ever so careful not to stare too hard at the attractive man in front of me. His rich dark molasses-colored eyes, which revealed signs of an inner mystery, would have surely made it impossible to take my eyes off of him if I watched him too long.

"Cool," he said, grabbing a bag from me anyway after seeing my obvious struggle, and then he followed me to my room.

"Dayum, folk. You're in I-30 too?" he asked as we reached the room. I dropped my bags in front of the door while I got out my key.

"Yeah."

"Cool, folk. Den I guess you's my new roommate."

I sat my bags down again after bringing them in the room and introduced myself. His rich, down south accent was kind of amusing. I had never really heard Southern expressions quite so thick before. It wasn't so heavy that he wasn't understandable, but just strong enough to know that he was definitely not from anywhere north of the Mason-Dixon.

The familiar scent of his cologne beckoned me as he pulled me in close after we shook hands and gave me one of those "wassup, half hugs". His body was bathed in Dolce & Gabbana, a scent I had worn myself a few times, but somehow it never smelled as intrinsic before today.

While secretly indulging in the sweetness of his scent for just a moment, I thought it was kind of ironic that we met like we did. I found it almost baffling that he was so willing to help a complete stranger, not knowing that he was my roommate. Had I been in his position, I don't think I would have been so perceptive or generous and probably would have walked on by.

"Jayson," I said, as I gave my new roommate a firm handshake.

"Doe-ray," my roommate said.

"Aiight, folk, I guess we should go git the rest of yo stuff."

"Aiight then."

I kept wondering what a "folk" was and why he kept saying it, but after a short time had past and he'd said it so much, I figured out that "folk" had to have been some sort of down south expression. There it was, less than 10 minutes since I had planted my feet on Georgia's soil, and I was already getting schooled in my first class: Country Grammar 101.

It only took Dorey and I a few minutes to unload everything I had in the car. After that, we came back to the room and relaxed for a few seconds before hearing a knock on our door. We had intentionally left it open so some fresh air could flow through the hot and tiny space.

There at the door stood a short, slim, light-skinned man with a huge smile.

"Do y'all need any help?" he asked, smiling, his eyes never leaving Dorey. Had it not been for the plural verbiage, I wouldn't have even known he saw me.

Dorey moved over to the door and, without saying a word, instantly slammed it shut. As he turned around, there was a look that birthed hatred plastered across his sweaty face.

"What was that about?" I asked, wondering why Dorey had shifted moods so abruptly. Until that point he had appeared to be one of the nicest people I'd met in a very long time, but now he seemed to be the direct opposite.

"He's a fuckin' fag! I can't stand fags. He's been hangin' 'round me all day, tryin' to make conversation. At first I thought he was cool 'til he started talkin' dumb out his mouth wit' sum old faggoty shit. He had me fooled, folk, thinkin' he was cool people, until he changed up on me. Damn faggot!"

"Oh, I didn't know it was like that," I said, trying, but failing, to hide the cringe I couldn't contain each time he said the word "fag" with so much loathing. I always hated that word, but the way he said it in his down South accent took my hatred to a new level.

Damn, there goes the possibility of me being able to be myself, I thought. I could see that I would have to hide my sexuality from this guy in order to avoid the same harsh treatment he had inflicted on the man at the door just a minute ago. From the looks of things, he had such a strong hatred toward gay people that I knew it was not going to be easy to live with him.

I wondered for a moment how long I could keep my secret from him, hoping it would be at least until I could get a new roommate.

After the brief interruption, we began to get to know each other, while I sorted through my belongings. Dorey had been on campus for two days, so he already had all of his things situated. Everything he had was unpacked, except for one or two bags and his bed was neatly made. My side of the room looked like something just short of a disaster in comparison, full of bags and unpacked luggage.

Not wanting to make a bad first impression, I got busy unpacking. Besides, the room was way too cramped to leave it so cluttered.

Dorey left while I was settling in and returned about an hour later with food. He must have read my mind, because my mouth began to water as he walked in trailed by the scent of hot fried chicken, which made my stomach roar.

"Thanks, yo, I'm starving." I said after he sat some chicken wings and fries down in front of me on my bed.

My new roommate was so nice, a little too nice, in comparison to what I was used to. Where I was from, people didn't usually display this sort of kindness for strangers. Back home people minded their own business pretty much keeping to themselves and looking out for their best interest before anyone elses.

Dorey's selfless actions left me feeling like there had to be some catch. First he helped me with my luggage and then brought me back some food after correctly assuming I would be hungry. Maybe this was just what people meant by Southern hospitality.

Way too hungry to try and figure out if there was anything suspicious lying dormant behind all of Dorey's random acts of kindness I began to eat.

"So, where you from, folk?" Dorey asked.

"Philly."

"Oh, alright. I'm from down here in the dirty, dirty, as we call it. I'm a born and bred Jo-giah boy."

"So you like it down here?"

"Yeah, it's cool so far, just hot as hell,"

"You'll git used to it, folk, trust me," he said, laughing.

He asked me to tell him a little bit about myself, so I gave him a brief synopsis of my life up until coming to Clark, leaving out the minor details of my sexuality and the estranged relationship with my father as a result of it. He in turn told me about his life, which seemed much more interesting. Although we were the same age, the picture he painted seemed to be in vivid color; mine on the other hand seemed black and white with a few shades of gray.

Dorey told me about his travels to other countries, that he spoke fluent French, Spanish and Italian. He also talked about his senior year of high school as a foreign exchange student in Italy and that he had just returned to the States for college.

My first impression of Dorey would have never led me to believe that he had so much culture and intelligence. He looked and acted more down-to-earth than most. After the short time I'd spent getting to know him, I'd already found out that he was so much more than the average Joe I had pegged him to be at first sight. I couldn't help but to wonder if his deep Southern accent came through with such force in foreign tongues as it did in English.

After looking around the room at all of his belongings, I figured he must have had money or he was dabbling in something illegal, because the big screen TV, DVD/VCR player and closet full of clothes definitely weren't representative of your typical college student.

When I commented on how nice his things were, he simply replied "I guess that's how it is when your parents have mo' money than they know whut to do with."

He told me his mother was a psychologist with a well-established roster of clientele and his dad was one of Atlanta's most prominent cardiologists. I also learned that his family was well connected with the "who's who" in the South, which consisted of the area's black elite.

Coming from a sheltered existence of a small section of Philadelphia, far from the better-known parts of the city, I was blown away by my roommate's impressive background.

Where I was from, you were said to "have it made" if you were out of your parent's house by the time you turned 25. That, along with several other reasons, was exactly why I had to leave home. My big time plans for my future far surpassed anything a small-town existence could ever offer, so I came to Atlanta, the so-called "place" to become somebody if you were young, black and driven.

Several hours passed, with Dorey and I talking the whole time. We talked about what our respective cities were like and joked about the many differences between the North and South. He told me that he would take me around Atlanta and show me the ropes.

My fears were settled and things were no longer scary. I had a roommate who was from Atlanta, had great connections and from what I knew of him so far, he seemed like a good-hearted person. Within that conversation I'd lost the urge to switch roommates. I would just have to over-look his mild case of homophobia, keep my secret tucked away, and things would be fine.

Dorey said he would be majoring in criminal justice and was at Clark on a track scholarship. He boasted big plans of one day becoming one of the best entertainment lawyers in the country, a career slightly fostered by his parents because of his strong love for music and a forbiddance by them to major in that area. After listening to his big dreams, I matched his goal by telling him that I was an English major and one day would become a famous writer.

Our competitive natures were introduced as we made a little friendly wager that was Dorey's idea. He said the first one of us to reach our goal would have to be paid a thousand dollars by the loser and get to gloat by saying "I told you so." Shaking hands, we sealed the deal, and on that day my roommate sparked an even bigger desire in me to succeed. My pride would not allow me to fail even if it was to someone as nice and cute as Dorey.

Being a native Georgian, Dorey had a lot of family and friends who were scattered throughout the area. Interestingly enough, he also had a one year-old daughter named Jasmine, who he said was the love of his life. Shortly after telling me about his daughter, he informed me of Jasmine's mom, who was still a big part of his life only because of their daughter. He didn't seem to revere her very much.

When Dorey asked me if I had a girlfriend or any kids, I quickly said 'no' and changed the subject. Obviously, Dorey didn't know I was gay and in that first conversation I wasn't ready for him to know it, either. Besides, he'd made his dislike for my kind quite clear. I didn't want to chance our developing friendship. However, I couldn't help but wonder again how long I could keep something like that from someone with whom I would be sharing so much of my time, not to mention a room.

3

"Hello"

"Hey Jayson. I just called to check on my baby and make sure you were doing ok."

"Yes Ma, things are great now. How are things back home?"

"Good, other than that fact that I miss you."

"Well I miss you too Ma. You should come to visit. I think you would really like Atlanta."

"Maybe… Well I have to go now, I will talk to you later. Did you get my last letter?"

"Yes, and I sent one to you yesterday."

"Okay baby. Love you."

The months whisked by without a trace of lingering. I couldn't help but notice that even though it felt like I had just moved to Atlanta, I was already halfway through my first semester. Just as time passed and the seasons changed, so did my life. I was feeling happiness for the first time in a while, and I loved every minute of it.

Life was kind. I was successfully balancing school and a budding social life. I'd put on 15 pounds of solid muscle while working out regularly at the school's gym, learned the city, met lots of new people, and spent most of my nights partying like there was no tomorrow.

Dorey and I were becoming what felt like best friends. We did everything together, hung out at the clubs, went to countless events held on and off campus, and when there was nothing else to do, we would just sit around and trip out with our fellow Clark comrades. But most times, it was just the two of us.

Even though Dorey and I spent incredible amounts of time together, hiding my sexuality was relatively easy, though it had started to weigh on my conscience. Occasionally, his homophobia would surface as he made comments about how he couldn't stand faggots whenever he saw someone who was openly gay. I would just brush the hatred off with a laugh, never once saying anything, though his bigoted words ran deep, striking a soft spot within me. Most times I changed the subject to try and divert his attention, but there was no diversion for me. The fact that he was so uncomfortable with the secret I was hiding left me conflicted.

Though I had not experienced sexual intercourse with a man, and was still naive to the homosexual lifestyle, I'd known I was gay for quite some time.

Some could question my self-assurance and security with who and what I was at such a young age, but the same certainty I had in the fact that I was human also brought un-contestable human desires.

My strong urge for the touch of a man was growing more intense. If hiding who I really was could only be as easy on the inside as it was on the outside, my mind would have been a much more peaceful place. It was like second nature keeping my private desires from becoming the public's knowledge, but trying to hide myself from myself was becoming a depressing game of hide and seek.

When the subject of females came up, I would use the same tired excuse about breaking up with my girlfriend before moving to Atlanta because she couldn't endure the strain of a long-distance relationship. Halfway into my story, I would go into a very convincing act, faking an undying love for this fictional woman who was "my first love". Though that story couldn't have been further from the truth and I hated lying, to my amazement, it worked every time. No one ever asked me any questions like why I didn't have a girlfriend or why I hadn't slept with any girls since I had been on campus. Most assumed because I was attractive and had females gravitating towards me constantly, that I was some sort of playboy, but if they only knew the truth.

The girls at Clark Atlanta were like sexpots, oozing with so much sexuality it made everyone take notice of their beauty. The boys on campus were young, dumb and full of cum, so there was undoubtedly lots of sex going on. It seemed like everyone but me was getting laid.

Masturbation seemed like the only outlet to release any stored sexual frustration, but playing with myself had become played out. This was the start of my college years, the time when being promiscuous was overlooked and even somewhat expected, but there I was, dateless, sexless, and sexually frustrated.

Every time I saw an attractive guy on campus my testosterone surged, bringing thoughts of what it would be like to have sex for the first time. Then, like clockwork, those thoughts were quickly replaced with the fear that rumors of my sexuality would be spread all over the school. If it ever got out that I'd slept with a man, I would be too embarrassed to continue at Clark and I just couldn't take that chance. Instead, I would silently lust and touch myself, fantasizing about the day I would eventually lose my virginity with someone who was as discrete as I was. I prayed many times that day would come sooner rather than later, because it was getting too hot and stuffy being all by myself in my lonely, self-constructed closet.

Pretty soon, everything changed. It was like my prayers had been answered and divine intervention had taken over.

The months of sharing a room with Dorey ran smoother than a well-oiled machine. We knew each other's routines like they were our own. Everything was perfect in my mind except for my inner issues with my sexuality and lack of sex. There was no drama, no chaos, and we never experienced any of the horror stories that I had heard around campus about how maniacal and conniving some roommate situations could get. Dorey never got in my way or left me with the feeling that I was being cramped, in spite of us always being so close.

Though I still hadn't experienced an actual relationship, on the inside I was often amused at how much it felt like I was married to my best friend. I knew more about him and was closer to him than any female he'd ever been with. We shared a space, ate together, laughed together; saw each other naked, and I knew his whereabouts almost every hour of the day. The only things keeping the two of us from having the traditional partnering between lovers were that Dorey was straight, we hadn't had sex, and there was no "relationship drama."

Wednesday nights, a group composed of me and five other students from my English literature class were required to meet up in a study session. The professor made this weekly "meeting of the minds" a mandatory part of the class and based a large percent of our grades on how effectively each group could work together to complete group projects. It seemed like nonsense, especially because no one took it seriously. Each week the sessions seemed more like a social event than the educational forum they were intended to be. When my group met up at the library, we'd spend half of the study session waiting for everyone to arrive. The remaining time was spent fooling around and cracking jokes, while Laana Johnson, the class know-it-all, completed whatever assignment we were given for the week, frustrated because no one else seemed to care.

This particular Wednesday was different. Laana was sick; meaning the study group would have to be canceled because without her, it was safe to say that nothing would get done.

After the meeting was called off, I grabbed some food from the cafeteria on my way back from the library before returning to my room.

The unmistakable scent of sweaty raw masculinity captured my senses, along with the almost-too–outrageous-to-be-true visions all around me. My jaw instantly hit the floor, along with the tray of Buffalo wings I had picked up from the dining hall. When I walked into my room that night, for a few moments I stood spellbound and wondered if I had accidentally come into the wrong dorm.

Every one of my five senses opened wide in that moment. My nose smelled the scent of sex, taste buds watered at the x-rated scene, and I could feel myself getting aroused as I heard moaning bouncing off the walls.

There on the TV screen was a cheesy porno playing, but that wasn't even halfway exciting compared to the rest of the details. The people on the screen were getting it on like beasts. And as far as the smell I walked in on, that came from Dorey and the stranger sharing a spot on his bed, as they seemed to be recreating what they saw on the television screen.

I was still shocked as I watched Dorey lying on his bed with his undressed ebony skin and another naked draping him. That figure had its head down around Dorey's waist and smooth, round ass high in the air. Its head moved up and down on Dorey's hard skin effortlessly, with the prowess of a porn star. Dorey's enjoyment was so strong with his eyes closed and hands on the person's head guiding it back and forth over his sex that he hadn't seen or heard me come in until the wings hit the floor with a splat.

Could I be dreaming? I wondered for a moment, but soon came assurance that this was reality as the non-roommate noticed my unwanted presence and looked up in terror.

The most scandalous revelation was that there were two familiar faces looking back at me, two male faces. While he was in between Dorey's legs, I couldn't tell from his curly hair, and slim curvaceous figure that he was a *he*. But as the boy looked at me seemingly frozen, I studied his face and became just as stunned. Dorey had always stood so firm in his opposition toward homosexuals, so I couldn't understand what I was witnessing.

The kid suddenly shot up like a bolt of lightning, almost knocking me down while running past me to get out of the room as quickly as he could while barely managing to put on his boxer briefs, leaving the rest of his clothes on the floor. This had to be one of the most unbelievable things I had ever experienced and it left me completely confused.

I had pegged Dorey to be the pretty boy/ jock type that had all the women he could handle, so I couldn't fathom what led him to cross over to the other side. He had never given me even the slightest inclination that he was gay, bisexual or would ever mess around with the same sex. I wondered to myself, was this just a one-time experiment or was the gay-ness that I had tried so hard to hide rubbing off onto him?

Growing up in a deeply religious family I heard many times that homosexuality was a demonic spirit, easily trans-ferred, but even after repeatedly hearing it, I never adopted that concept. For as long as I could remember, I felt an attraction to the same sex. However, what I cannot recall is ever spreading my preference to anybody else. In fact, the last time I checked I hadn't found any documentation to back up their belief that homosexuality was a contagious virus or disease like the plague, AIDS or flu. I always felt it was something that was either in you or not, and it was as simple as that. So with that in mind, my questioning of Dorey's actions only grew.

Reveling in the pleasant but painful moment that had just taken place, I hid my emotions well. I almost wanted to do a victory dance because it felt like something incredible had happened. I was stunned, but happy at the same time. Now it would be so much easier to open up to Dorey and tell him all my secrets. I no longer feared that Dorey would ex-communicate me if I told him about my sexuality because we were now guilty of the same crime. I felt so much better, but in my happiness I didn't stop to think about Dorey. He had to be embarrassed and feeling horrible.

Questioning why Dorey had never told me about this part of him, I continued to stand in disbelief. If this wasn't just a one-time thing, why hadn't he told me? Then I thought about how long I'd hidden my truth from him, gave up wondering why and focused on where we would go from there.

Walking right past Dorey, I said "wassup" and sat my books down on the bed like I had seen nothing, heard nothing and felt absolutely nothing.

While cleaning up the mess I made on the floor, I wasn't even the least bit upset that I had nothing to eat. In my excitement, my empty stomach was the furthest thing from my mind. Dorey sat silently on the corner of his bed, still naked except for the puzzled look on his face. Should I say something? I wondered if now was the time to try talking to him, or if it was best to continue pretending that nothing shocking or odd just went down until he showed signs of wanting to confess.

After about an hour passed, It felt like if I was to bite my tongue for even a second longer, I would have chewed right through. Before speaking I put myself in his shoes and thought about what I would want Dorey to say if it was me lying naked on that bed. After thinking long and hard over what to say, I realized I didn't have the right words. Secretly hoping for that moment, yet never thinking it would ever come, it came and found me prepared. Maybe it *was* best to just continue as if nothing had happened and suffer the consequences of my chosen silence.

Obviously Dorey wasn't in a talkative mood, so we continued breathing in silence that night, no television, no music, no sound at all, just breathing and a lot of thinking.

Before falling asleep, I must have relived that scene of Dorey exposed on his bed about 50 times. After the many mental replays of that moment, I suddenly realized why the other boy's face looked so familiar. Not only was he the boy who I had seen my first day on campus as the door slammed shut in his face, but he was also the same boy who was in a few of my classes. His name was Jarvis Thurman. Although I had never really paid that much attention to Jarvis before that night, I had a funny suspicion he wouldn't go unnoticed so easily in the future.

As if that evening had not already had its fair share of excitement, the adrenaline-prompting action wasn't quite through. Strangely, something was going bump in the night, literally waking me with audible, violent thuds of what sounded like something struggling for breath in between pain-drenched sobs that filled the confines of the dark room.

I shot up from my bed and turned on the light.

No sooner than the room was illuminated did Dorey's body immediately capture my attention. As he lay in his bed, his body struggled with itself uncontrollably, as if he were fighting an intense battle in which he was the only opponent. With balled hands, his fists and arms were so tense that raised veins filled almost every inch of them. I watched in shock, looking into his partially open eyes. They were released just enough to see the evidence that he was slipping away to some far off place far beyond the room, and they were full of tears. That sad sight of my roommate sent me into a panic.

While my unnerved hands toiled in a pathetic attempt to dial 9-1-1, I yelled out to Dorey in a voice that was shaking just as badly as my hands.

"Dorey it's going to be okay!"

The wait for someone to answer on the other end of the phone seemed everlasting. When someone finally came through the line saying, "9-1-1, what is your emergency?" all I could do was demand that someone come to the Clark Atlanta dorms a.s.a.p., giving the lady my hall and room numbers without even a 'hello.'

The soothing voice of the operator sensed my loss of control and tried to reassure me that everything was going to be okay. But in my current frenzy, I didn't want to hear anything but the sounds of the paramedics knock. She attempted to ask questions slowly and calmly, but there were no answers that I could give. I had no idea of what was happening.

"It looks like my roommate is dying!" I yelled.

"Is he breathing?" she asked.

"Yes! Barely. He's gasping like he's choking or something, shaking really bad and in pain!"

There was no way that Dorey's loud cries could have gone unnoticed. By that point, he was yelling so loud that someone had come pounding on our door with such force it should have come unhinged. I raced over to open the door and it was Kevin, the Resident Advisor on our floor. He asked if everything was okay with an unmistakable look of horror on his usually blank face. As Kevin and I both watched Dorey convulse in the background we knew, clearly everything was not okay.

I tried desperately to juggle information between Kevin and the operator until it was evident that the operator needed much more attention.

Kevin rushed to Dorey's bed, trying to consol the pain and now sweat drenched Dorey by telling him that everything was going to be okay and that help was on the way. But Dorey was still off in his own world where pain reigned supreme, clearly unaware of anything going on around him.

After giving all the information requested by the 9-1-1 operator, she informed me that the ambulance had been dispatched about five minutes ago and should be arriving at any moment.

By that time, Dorey's hollering had awakened just about everyone on our floor, causing a crowd to form slowly outside our door. Watching for a moment as the crowd continued to grow in, Kevin then went over to dispatch them, assuring everyone that everything was being taken care of and asked them to go back to their rooms while we continued to wait for help.

A collective, sweet sigh of relief escaped our bodies as two paramedics rushed into the room, asked a few questions, and then rolled Dorey's barely conscious body out of the room on a stretcher almost as fast as they had arrived.

After Dorey was secure in the ambulance, the door was shut and it drove off with a loud siren blaring. The bright, flashing lights of the ambulance sped off into the distance un-

til eventually slipping into the darkness of night while my
worries grew.

4

Sometimes waiting can seem an impossible feat, especially when that wait is for something you desire so strong it becomes heartrending.

My thoughts became centered around Dorey and his health was my key concern. I lost focus of everything else around me and suddenly my best friend was all that mattered.

I didn't see Dorey for a few days after the night he was carried to the hospital. The wait slowly broke me down with each passing day, and each day was filled with growing uncertainty and worry.

I went to the hospital several times during those days of wait—just about every free moment I had between classes—was spent hanging around hoping for the ability to find out if he was all right. But each time, I was given a new excuse by many different nurses as to why I couldn't see him.

At first I was told they were running tests and was assured that once the tests were completed I would be able to see him. Those evaluations preceded more tests, more excuses, and then even more tests and reasons why I still couldn't see Dorey. Though torn that I hadn't seen him, at least I knew he was alive.

At long last, the wait was finally over. After three days and countless unproductive visits, I was given Dorey's room number instead of another unwanted "No."

Strangely, I wasn't overwhelmingly relieved to finally be granted the opportunity to see Dorey. Wasn't this is why I had been commuting back and forth for days? However, instead of relief, this shaky, unnerving feeling attacked me as I slowly walked toward his room. What if he was barely alive, still fighting for life or hooked to all kinds of machines? Was I strong enough to see him like that?

As I turned the corridor and was about to knock on his door, which was halfway open, I heard Dorey's familiar laugh, instantly calming me. He was sitting up in bed, holding his daughter Jasmine. The room didn't seem big enough to contain the bright smiles on both of their faces and the love exchanged between them.

On the edge of the bed sat a lady I had never seen, but judging by her unmistakable resemblance to Dorey, I knew it had to be his mother.

"Can I come in?" I asked, as I walked in slowly.

"Wassup," Dorey and Jasmine said, almost in one voice, as I walked closer to the bed.

"This is my mother. Mah, this is my best friend Jayson. And Jay, you already know Jasmine," Dorey said.

"It's nice to meet you," I said, giving Dorey's mom a hug.

"It's good to meet you, too," she said, squeezing me tight enough to make me feel like I was one of her own children.

Dorey's mom went on to tell me in her subdued Southern accent that she had heard a lot about me, thanked me for taking care of her son, then asked me a few questions like how I liked Atlanta and college. We continued talking for little while longer until being interrupted.

"Come on, Mah! He didn't come to get interrogated. He came to see me," Dorey said, smiling.

"Okay, okay! I guess I will let you two have some peace. I need to be getting home to cook anyways. Oh, and

Dorey, I'm cooking your favorite! Lasagna! But, since you're kicking me out, you already know I won't be bringing you any, right?" she said, with a wink and a smile.

We all started laughing as Dorey's mom said good-bye and walked out of the room, hand in hand with Jasmine.

"So I'm your best friend?" I quizzed, already knowing the answer.

"Yeah, you already know you are my peoples. Besides, I don't know too many other people who would have looked out for me like you did the otha' night. You might have saved my life. And I think that deserves best friend status."

"Your mom is cool people," I said.

"Yeah, she's alright, I guess. I'm just glad you came when you did because she was about to give me the blues about takin' betta care of myself. I already know it. If you wouldn't have come, she would have been here 'til midnight givin' me the same old lecture that I've heard at least fifty times before."

"So what was wrong?" I asked, watching Dorey's mood instantly change.

"I'm sorry about the otha' night," Dorey said.

The last time that Dorey and I had seen each other so much unfolded. I wasn't really sure what part of that evening he was apologizing for, but an apology was unnecessary.

"You don't have to apologize to me," I said.

"The doctors say I was experiencin' some complications from my leukemia that made me spaz like that."

"Leukemia?" I asked.

"Yes. I was diagnosed with leukemia when I was sixteen. Long story short, I've been through all types of treatments and I was in remission for about 2 years, but now some of the cancer is back. The doctors say it's minor and fully treatable so don't worry. It's no big thing. I feel fine now and I'm just ready to get outta' this bed.

Stunned and not sure of what to say, silence now fell upon me while sitting there on his bed. In my uncontrollable daze, I made a mental note to research leukemia as soon as possible. I wasn't quite sure of the details of the disease, but really didn't want to ask Dorey at such an already awkward moment. Whatever it was that he had, I knew it couldn't be good.

"So does that make me gay?"

That question shot from Dorey's mouth, unbridled and unexpectedly, removing the lid from the silence in the room and instantly changed the focus of our conversation, digressing from his illness to exactly the subject I wanted to avoid.

"Does what make you gay?" I asked, with false ignorance.

Only a few days had passed since the night Dorey was caught in that rather embarrassing and compromising position with Jarvis. I probably would have continued to pretend that evening never existed had he not brought it up, because I had settled things in my mind. Now there we were, confronting the shocking truth.

I thought for a few minutes about what to say in response, but kept drawing blanks. That was one of those questions that did not have a right or wrong answer.

"I don't know," I said, as I got up to check if his door was shut. All I needed was for his mother or one of his other family members to walk in on this candid conversation.

Just then, a young, female nurse entered the room, smiling, letting us know that she was there to check on Mr. Braxton. Her presence brought me a few much-needed minutes to think about what I could say to Dorey, knowing as soon as she left, he would resume the previous discussion without skipping a beat. Sure enough, no sooner then the nurse closed the door behind her he started talking.

"Well, I've been havin' these crazy feelin's inside of me for the longest time that have been buildin'. It's like somethin' tells me that I'm wrong for feelin' the way I do because of what everyone else says 'bout it. But at the same time, it doesn't feel completely wrong ... I was like twelve years old and me and one of my cousins, Travis, would fool around. This was before I was old enough to know right from wrong. Travis was my favorite cousin. He was two years older than me and was, in many ways, like the big brother I never had. We spent a lotta time together, especially since our parents were always workin'. It was never really an issue to me and I never really thought about what we were doin' 'til I got older. But even when I was old enough to know what we were doing was wrong the feelings never went away. A few years later, I was molested by one of my father's good friends from church and I never told a soul. I try to block all of that from my mind. That probably has a lot to do with why I *say* I hate fags so much. Every time I see one, part of me remembers my daddy's friend and the sick things he did to me. The otha night was the first time in *years* that I'd done anything with a man. I guess I was trying to see if the thoughts in me were just thoughts or if there was still more to it."

Captivation! Dorey caught me off guard as he sat there opening up about his past and sharing with me things he had never exposed. Spellbound and unprepared for this conversation, yet I was elated to receive confirmation that I was no longer alone. No longer would I have a reason to hide my total self from him, because the struggle with our sexuality was yet again something the two of us shared, albeit secretly. It was awkward sitting there listening to Dorey talk and show the vulnerable side of himself that I had never seen. Soon, I knew it would be my turn to open up.

"I feel the same things that you do," I said, interrupting his story. Suddenly, this unstoppable surge of truth shot from my tongue, forcing me to come clean. My fear was that if I didn't say it then, the opportunity to tell him might not have presented itself again.

"What do you mean?" Dorey asked, seeming puzzled.

"I mean, I feel the same thing that you do. The truth is Dorey, the playboy that everybody thinks I am, the ex-girlfriend I said I had back home… All lies. The only thing is I've never really acted on my urges, but I know what I want. I don't need to have sex or hide behind labels to define who and what I am. Ever since I was 10, I've known about this part of me that made me feel somewhat abnormal, but I've tried so hard to keep it a secret because of what my family thinks, what my friends think, what my religion says, what society says. It got overwhelming at times, denying myself the right to be me just for the sake of making those around me happy while I lived in pain. But, I've done it for years, so trust me, I know how you feel. I wanted to tell you the truth a long time ago. The only reason I didn't was because I value your friendship and you always talked so bad about gay people," I said.

"That's out of insecurity and pain. I like girls, and I like guys. I don't like any one betta than the otha, but when I have sex with a girl, it's different because I never have to worry about who is gon' find out, unless she's ugly. But when I did what I did the otha night, although it felt good, in the back of my mind, I feared gettin' caught, and that's exactly what happened," Dorey said.

"Don't stress yourself over it. Look, if you want I will continue to act like that night never even happened," I said.

"But it did happen, Jay, and now it's like I'm ashamed of myself in so many ways. I'm mad at myself for lettin' it happen, I'm mad at myself for enjoyin' it, and I'm mad at myself for wantin' to do it again."

"Why should you be mad at yourself?"

"Because it ain't right."

"Since when is being proud of who you are wrong?"

"Since it's an abomination of God, that's when."

"Look, Dorey, I know it's hard for you to deal with this, but like I told you, I've been dealing with it a while. I'm not saying that I'm right or that you're wrong. All that I'm saying is that someday, if you continue to beat yourself up over it, you will reach your boiling point. The point where you say, 'enough is enough' and either go crazy or finally make peace. My boiling point already arrived. Though I've been hiding it, I still know what I am and I'm to the point where I'm cool with it. I got tired of being depressed and beating myself up over hating a part of myself that I had no real control of. It had me at a point where I was so conflicted I didn't want to live. I felt like I was not worthy of life just because I was gay.

"One night I actually prayed to God that He either make me straight or kill me. I prayed all night, tears rolling down my face, for either one of those two things to happen, believing wholeheartedly that I was ready for either outcome. But guess what? In the morning, I was alive and still as gay as the night before. That morning, I realized that I was more than just my sexuality. Since I was still alive I figured there must be a purpose for why my life was spared, and I vowed to no longer beat myself up over something that was such a small part of me. Instead, I slowly started to embrace everything about myself because that's what makes me who I am.

"It wasn't easy and it took a long time for me to love my whole self, but after doing so, I haven't once looked back. Before all of that happened I was a mess, living my life for everyone else and in turn, everyone enjoyed me but me. I felt like I had to portray this fictitious character to the world, just to keep everyone content, even though it was tearing me apart inside, living that lie. I was denying myself of life, *my* life. I realized everyone gets one life that *they* have to live, and by letting everyone else around me control my life, I was giving them *too* much control, sending me out of control. *They* were living my life, *they* were writing my story *their* way. Dorey, you know I want to be a writer. Now how does that look? Letting someone else write my story? No one can tell my life story better than me, so why should I let someone co-write or be the author of a tale best told by me? I'm not telling you to feel like I do, but everyone has to do what works for them in this thing called life."

I finished slightly out of breath after slipping into a preachy mode. I had been talking nonstop for the last few minutes, which shocked me, because when I first started speaking I had no clue what I was going to say.

"Damn," was all Dorey could say in response to my longwinded soliloquy.

After a few minutes of silence and reflecting on our conversation, Dorey asked, "So how do you know that you're gay if you never have had sex with a man?"

"I've never told anyone this," a long silence proceeded while I relived the story I was about to tell and tried to gather my thoughts.

"Are you okay?" Dorey asked.

"February the eighteenth. It's odd how I remember everything about that day with vivid detail, even the date. I was a senior in high school and on that day during fifth period, we were playing a game of flag football in gym.

"The game was intense, leaving most of the players dripping with sweat and funk afterward. After staying back instead of heading into the locker room to change and get ready for the next period, the gym teacher, Coach Wilson, instructed me and another student, Devin Brown, to help clean up the equipment and put everything back in the storage closet."

"It only took us about five minutes to pick everything up and put it away, but we wasted time afterward, trying to avoid our next class for as long as possible.

"As a result of playing so hard, I was kind of funky and decided to take a shower.

"After a few minutes of enjoying the steam-filled shower, I realized I wasn't alone. Devin had come walking into the shower area where I was, wrapped in a red towel.

"This strange feeling came over me. After he slowly undid the towel from his body, I couldn't help but notice that his physique was very defined compared to my slim frame and I was envious. His muscles were sculpted and seemed to fill every inch of his body. As I continued to watch him from the corner of my eye, I became both jealous and intrigued. He looked so beautiful there in the shower with the water streaming down his picture-perfect body.

"Devin and I were cool. I'd met him during a very brief cameo on the track team in my sophomore year and we had been cool ever since. Though I'd known him for a while, that day I was introduced to a new side of Devin.

"I felt embarrassed, because I knew he had caught me staring. To make it even worse, I started to feel myself getting hard. I tried to hide myself by turning around in the other direction, but it was no use. I expected Devin to leave the shower once he saw that I was looking at him with my uncontrollable erection, and go spread the word through the school that I was a sissy and how I was in the shower staring at him on hard. That didn't happen. Instead, he came closer until he was at the shower next to mine. Devin turned on the water and started to wash his body as if nothing out of the ordinary was taking place. I also acted like everything was normal, trying to take my mind off of his body to give mine a chance to calm down. I caught myself staring again. This time, two things were different. One, he was staring back at me, and two; his dick was now just as hard as mine.

"He came even closer until I could almost feel his body heat on me overcoming the heat from the hot water of the shower. He asked if he could use my soap because he didn't have any. I agreed.

"As I reached out to hand it to him, he grabbed my hand, intentionally holding it tight, prompting my heart to race. I looked at him with a strange look in my eyes as I tried to figure him out. He still was holding my hand and brought it toward his body, slowly closer until our skin touched.

"With my hand now on his lower stomach and still in his grasp, he started moving it in a slow, circular motion.

"He tried to ease our hands down lower until I was almost touching his dick but I suddenly jumped back. Surely what we were doing wasn't right. But, oddly enough, it didn't feel wrong. It was a little strange and I didn't understand it.

"Looking back, I would love to say that we had some sort of erotic, lovemaking session that day in the shower, or that after that day, he became my first boyfriend, we started secretly dating, having sex and the whole nine. None of those things ever happened. The only thing that came about after that day was Coach Wilson seeing us without our knowledge. That night he called both of our parents to let them know what happened, which resulted in a tragic, ass whooping given to me by my father and it is still straining our relationship to this day. As for Devin, he quickly transferred schools and I never saw him again," I said.

I paused a moment to catch my breath.

"Even before that day in the shower with Devin, I knew the feelings inside of me were real. However, it wasn't until that day that things solidified in my mind. The part of that whole ordeal that let me know without a shadow of a doubt I was gay was this: After the first fight with my father, after he found out about Devin, the torture didn't stop there. He started beating me for everything. He beat me for living, he beat me for breathing, he would beat me after a hard day of work, and any excuse he could find to hit me. I guess he figured he could maybe beat the gayness out of me. But even enduring his sick torture wasn't enough to change my ways. My body became his personal punching bag, leaving me with bruises and scars all over my body. Some have faded; some will probably never go away. I said all that to say if my father's brutality wasn't strong enough to make me straight, I doubted anything else in the world would be.

"It was hell for me up until I came here for school, which is why I can't go back."

Dorey remained speechless, until saying the only few words he spoke for the rest of that day.

"I hope I never meet his ass. I will kill him for hurting you!"

In the days that followed, we ended up having lots more discussions mirroring the one in the hospital. We opened up more and more to each other until we were so close, I felt like I had known Dorey my whole life.

Though we were two different people with many contrasts, we shared the universal pain felt by most people who questioned their sexuality in a world that seemed like it was meant for anyone but them.

Our friendship had reached a new plateau.

5

I want to see you at the Downtown Ritz Carlton Hotel this Saturday night, February fourteenth, at eight o'clock. Leave a message on the voicemail at 678.555.1212 to let me know if you can make it. Hope to see you soon.

Your secret admirer

After a busy day of classes, this fancy-looking note had been slipped under the door, instantly catching my attention. It was in a beige envelope with a thin, gold ribbon wrapped around it and my name in intricate gold script.

Could this be some type of joke?

I was flattered by the invitation and deeply interested in knowing who had gone through what seemed like a lot of effort with such a delivery. It seemed almost too good to be true, so I tossed the letter on my bed, brushing it off as nothing more than a secret crush that would never amount to anything.

"What's this?" Dorey asked.

By the time Dorey had entered the room, I was so entranced with studying for a big calculus test that I did not hear him come in. His words almost went unheard.

"Huh?" I asked, looking up from my book as Dorey plopped his body down on the edge of my bed. He was looking over something he held closely in his hands.

It was the note from earlier, sent by my secret admirer. Its receipt had completely slipped my mind in the midst of all my hard-core studying.

"Oh, that's nothing. Just something that was under the door when I got in," I said, continuing to downplay it.

"Doesn't look like nothin'. Says here you have a secret admirer. And it looks like whoever it is must like you a lot because they want you to meet them at the Ritz Carlton. That place is expensive," he said, showing a hint of what almost sounded like jealousy.

I just laughed at Dorey's comment and continued not to feed into the invitation, as my mind stayed on preparing for my test. Soon my attention fell back into my thick math book and I started trying to memorize formulas. Deep into the books contents, I could hear Dorey still speaking in the background, but I couldn't fully make out anything he was saying. He sensed that I was in the zone after I didn't respond to him. He got up from the bed, placing the note back in the same spot where he found it.

"So are you going to go?" he asked loudly.

Looking up, I saw him gathering all his bathroom supplies and quickly undress, throwing a towel around his body. He awaited my answer.

"No, I'm not about to go spend a night in a hotel with a stranger."

"You just might enjoy yourself. I mean, you said the otha day you've never had a valentine, so here is your chance. You should definitely go," he said very convincingly and gave me a quick wink of his eye before heading off to the showers.

I pondered his suggestion a moment before going back to studying, and then it hit me. It was Dorey! I just realized after he left the room that it was he who sent the invitation. Somehow what should have been blatantly obvious went unnoticed. Dorey was one of the only few students on campus who had enough money to pull off a night at the Ritz. Anyone else would have been pressed just to scrounge up enough for a measly box of candy and possibly a teddy bear, if they were really splurging.

The effects of the long talks we were having and the time we shared must have been mutual. I held a secret attraction for Dorey since our inception. However, unsure that his feelings would ever have been reciprocated, I continued to hide my feelings. Over time, the friendship we developed had become more than enough for me. Besides, if our friendship suffered because of unreciprocated emotions, I would have been devastated.

Now was the chance I had been waiting for. The timing couldn't have been any better if it were scripted, so I picked up the phone and dialed the number on the invitation to let him know that I would be there at 8 p.m. sharp.

After a few rings, an automated voicemail took the call. It was a robotic-sounding, female voice saying, "Please leave, your name and number after the beep."

I left a short message saying that I had decided to take them up on their invitation and would be there Saturday night. About fifteen minutes later, Dorey entered the room, grinning from ear to ear. When I asked why he was smiling so hard he just replied "nothin". He quickly finished drying himself off and got dressed, occasionally giving me a devilish look that let me know he was definitely up to something. Yeah, with a look like that, he had to be my secret admirer, I thought to myself.

Valentine's Day finally arrived. As a result of the anticipation that had been building, there were butterflies in my stomach so big that they felt more like tiny kick boxers.

I greeted the hotel's concierge with a smile. He was standing behind the desk in the lobby with a smile that was matched by mine. It looked as if he was hanging on my every word as I introduced myself.

"Im Jayson Story. I'm supposed to be meeting someone here at 8.

"Oh yes, Mr. Story! Welcome to the Ritz Carlton. Your room is 828. I hope you enjoy your stay," he said, continuing to smile as he handed me a room key that resembled a credit card.

"828," I kept saying to myself while waiting for the elevator.

My nervous energy almost consumed me as the elevator opened and I stepped inside, greeted by a small man with a big grin. "What floor, sir?" he asked.

"8," I said, as he pushed the corresponding button and we watched the highly polished, brass doors close. On the door's shiny surface staring back at me was my worried reflection.

"828," I repeated, while searching the corridor for my room and anxiously wondering what Dorey had in store.

Looking at the numbers that read "828" on the door of the room was also a note that said, "Come in and follow the directions."

I took the note from the door and entered the room to see it drenched with romantic ambiance. There were candles everywhere, a bouquet of fresh flowers and flower petals scattered on the floor in a trail leading to the bed. I looked around at the beauty of the room for a moment and almost forgot that Dorey wasn't there, so caught up in the exquisite surroundings.

On the bed was another note lying atop a small package, wrapped in shiny, gold paper. The note said, simply, "Open." Tearing the gold paper from the small box and opening it, I found there on the inside a cell phone with another note that said, "This is part one of your Valentine's gift because I know you needed it. You already know the number. Part two will come when you take everything you have on off, and go get your next note that's waiting in the closet."

This is getting kind of fun, I thought as I quickly got naked and tiptoed on a trail of anticipation leading to my next clue. There, sure enough, was another note waiting for me.

"Put this robe on and meet me in the bathroom, and hurry up. I've been waiting!"

Following the last note's instructions, I sprinted into the bathroom full of excitement that had replaced every trace of nervousness.

My jaw fell and my eyes grew wide as I entered the bathroom to find a rather unexpected sight. I pulled my robe tightly shut covering what had been exposed and tried to disappear into its thick, white, terrycloth material.

Standing before me was a man who clearly wasn't Dorey. He looked about 40 years older and 40 pounds lighter. And though we were both occupying the bathroom, he looked like he could surely stand a shower more than I. A coarse, salt-and-pepper beard caught my eye as the gentleman said "hello." Somebody should have warned me that I was getting fixed up with the dude, Grady from "Sanford and Son," and I would have stayed my non-date-having ass home, I thought to myself as my lips barely managed to mumble "hello."

Standing there, frozen in disbelief, I didn't quite know what to do. The way he looked at me was starting to make me feel uneasy.

"Um, excuse me, sir, but who are you?" I asked, as I examined the old man.

"I'm Horace, your secret admirer," he said in a low shaky voice, coming closer to me.

"No you're not!" I demanded. With each step Horace made in my direction, I took one back, moving away from him.

"Oh, now Jayson, don't even act like that. Show an old man some love," he pleaded, still continuing to inch his way closer to me as I moved away.

Just then a loud burst of uncontrollable laughter came from inside the linen closet to my right. The laughter sounded familiar. When I opened the door, there was Dorey, doubled over in hysteria. He was so amused that if his dark, brown skin could blush he would have been turning bright red.

Still reeling from his prank, I couldn't have been happier to see him, and know that Horace was only a bad joke. My assumption about Dorey being having and interest in me was correct.

"Thank you, Horace, I appreciate you helpin' me out," Dorey said, as he exited the closet, still laughing so hard that tears had began to form in his eyes.

"Sure thing, brother. Y'all be cool and take it light," Horace said, taking his cue to exit stage left. On his way out he mumbled under his breath some things that were barely audible. I thought I heard him say something about "fudge packing." But it really didn't matter. I just laughed it off and began to hug Dorey.

"You should have seen your face. That was priceless." Dorey said.

"What was that all about anyway?" I asked.

"Horace was out on the street when I was on my way over here askin' me for some spare change. I told him that I would hook him up if he didn't mind doin' me a favor in return. You knew, and I knew you knew, that I was your secret admirer so, I had to do somethin' to throw you off. It couldn't be that easy for you. I gave Horace twenty dollars and told him what I wanted and in turn we scared the shit outta you!" Dorey said.

"Yeah, I admit you got me."

"Oh, I got you?" he asked, coming closer to me as I watched the smile in his eyes vanish inside a look of lust. He gave me a big hug and as we touched and I inhaled his scent, I could tell he was nervous by his embrace. To be honest, I had become nervous once again as well, and my nerves didn't have me shaking because of the stunt with Horace. There, in Dorey's arms, my heart started racing because this was going to be my first time.

"Now, take off that robe," Dorey whispered seductively in my ear right before releasing me from his captivity.

Standing there completely naked, I watched as Dorey further heightened the mood already evoked by lighting a single candle and turning off the lights in the bathroom.

Without words to cramp the atmosphere, he turned on the water to the bathtub, poured in an entire jar of bath beads, then scooped me up and placed me on the sink's marble countertop.

While waiting for the tub to fill, he started to kiss me for the first time. With our first kiss, there was reassurance, letting me know that this feeling coming over me was okay.

Kissing him felt so right that it became like second nature. I suddenly lost all fear of what was to come. Before that kiss, I was mildly afraid, filled with uncertainty and wondering. But as nature began to take its course without any coercion necessary, it all started making sense.

The golden-amber flame burning from the candlelight filled the room with a soft glow that almost danced around us, mimicking the candle's fire. The light was mellow but intense, kinetic and almost electric. Our shadows filled the walls and after a few moments, our flame was almost hotter than that of the candle. The passion had become so hot and unbridled that our actions combined with the heat of the hot bathwater running covered the walls with a dewy veil.

The mirror in back of me had become foggy from the steam and sweat poured over our brows. I felt reincarnated as the fire of the burning candle. I was burning up on the inside yet we had only just started to kiss.

A split second later, all of Dorey's clothes were in a small mound gathered next to him and we were both standing in front of each other with just smiles and longing to cover our naked flesh.

Our bodies had become pressed so tightly together that it was hard to distinguish who was who. Never before had someone been able to bring out so many feelings in me as he did that night. My senses came alive and amplified continuously as the night wore on. It was almost as if a drug was pumping through my veins, taking over and leaving me totally powerless while riding its forbidden high.

We began to firmly grind our bodies together without so much as a thought of space between us, which sent chills racing up and down my spine.

Dorey then motioned me to enter the tub after comfortably placing his body in. I submerged myself into the calming fluid that was at just the right temperature and he began to bathe me. He started with my neck and shoulders, working his hands lightly across them, gently massaging me while his hands glided effortlessly across my soapy frame and all my cares were cleansed.

Then, he moved down a little further, slowly rubbing my chest and back without leaving one spot untouched from the time he had started at my neck until he started to make circles with his fingers around my belly button. Taking a brief pause, he stared me deeply in the eyes before proceeding with his seductive massage. Taking one hand and putting it over my face while the other still explored my body, I closed my eyes and grew weak, as he had reached my most sensitive spot.

He took my sex into his hand and started massaging it just as he had done for the rest of my body. Dorey started with delicacy, gently moving his hand up and down my sex, slowly increasing the vigor of his movement until he had reached a speed and pressure that felt sensational. My body squirmed with pleasure from left to right in the water.

His soft whisper in my ear along with his cooling breath increased the level of my arousal. He watched for a moment while I enjoyed him, and then continued speaking words in my ear. In between his words he used his tongue to taste and caress the insides of each ear. I could hear every breath he took, which was filled with the ultimate air of passion. The alluring way his raw sexuality was displayed so far that night, coupled with the things he continued to divulge, were turning me on so much it was almost unbearable.

Unable to hold my emotions in any longer, I moaned uncontrollably seconds after Dorey rested my head on his chest, spread my legs apart, and began to slide a finger ever so gently inside of me. With one hand still on my sex and the other penetrating, the combination was becoming too intense to remain mute.

Looking around the dimly lit room, I could first see our silhouettes on the wall shadowing our every move then our reflection in the large mirror on the wall. The ultimate turn-on was watching in the misted mirror as we continued pleasing each other's bodies and the look on Dorey's face he made every time I touched a spot that he liked.

We finished our bubble bath and followed the trail of flower petals on the floor to the bed, lying there while the air slowly dried our moist skin, unsure of what to do next. We struggled for dominance for a few moments until I gave in and decided to let Dorey be the aggressor. I quickly wanted to rethink my decision as he started trying to explore me.

There was an intense stinging sensation as he parted my walls and slowly tried to ease his way inside. It burned so much I had to pull back and stop things for a moment to cool myself. The feeling was similar to someone lighting a match to my skin.

I had no idea that something that I wanted so much would hurt so badly. After the pain of the first attempt and a few moments of deep kissing, Dorey tried to slide inside of me again. This time it was much less painful, yet still not fully pleasurable. The girth of Dorey's erection took some time and effort to get used to, but after a few moments of positioning and repositioning, the pleasure released.

Grabbing my ankles, he placed one of my feet on each side of his shoulders, resting them there as he held the front of my thighs and we moved back and fourth in a fluid motion. As he bore his weight down on me and began caressing my chest, he then began to address my nipples. He took a few moments on each side, teasing each with the warmth of his tounge. I grabbed his waist and pulled him even deeper inside of me.

The pleasure had grown too intense for Dorey to withstand, because after only a few more thrusts and some heavy breathing, he had lost control, reaching climax and collapsing on top of me.

Even though this was my first time, I was certain that it was supposed to last longer.

"Sorry, that was my fault. It was feeling so good. Your ass is so damn tight," he said, looking disappointed as if he had let me down.

"It's all right," I said, as I looked at him smiling, trying to mask my amusement. The fact was that even though it had only lasted a short time, and most of that time was spent trying to get everything situated, I wasn't the least bit disappointed. The night was so mind-blowing already. The hotel room, the flowers, the candles, the romance, the massage, the man. Laying there with Dorey, after he had given me so many incredible things was more than enough for me.

After a few minutes, Dorey was ready to try things again, and soon we were back at it. That time it lasted much longer and it was nothing short of spectacular.

6

There it was, already one o' clock in the afternoon. The day was slipping away, yet Dorey and I were still in the bed lounging, with the sound of the television humming in the background and no plans of budging on our minds. It was an extraordinary Saturday where I had nothing to do, no studying and no papers. For a change I could just relax.

I was enjoying Dorey's strong embrace while nestled firmly into the crook of his arm and watched quietly as he drifted in and out of sleep.

Ever since Valentine's Day at the Ritz Carlton, we had become inseparable. We'd always shared a big part of our days, but now each night our beds resembled our lives. We would push our two twin-sized beds together, making one big bed until morning.

Dorey opened his eyes, looked over, noticed I was watching him, and positioned himself so that he was facing me. After a few seconds he looked in my eyes, and then asked,

"So, have you decided what you're gon' to do for the summer?"

"No," I replied, thrown off by his question and becoming slightly depressed, because time flew by and left me unprepared. The first week in May, which was less than two weeks away would mark the end of the semester. It also meant I would have to vacate my dorm room shortly after and I still had no idea where I was going to spend my summer vacation.

All that I was sure of was that going home was not an option. Staying the summer at a shelter or the local YMCA sounded like heaven in comparison to Pennsylvania. I just couldn't bring myself to go home to the same chaotic surroundings I had left.

I still didn't feel safe around my father, and didn't want to be around him or the painful memories the sight of him would induce. Besides, I had vowed not to go back until I could prove him wrong.

When I left for college, my father basically cursed me. While looking in his eyes right before leaving with his icy stare, he told me that I brought him nothing but shame, would never amount to anything and, in so many words, was not welcome back after I left. So I promised myself that the next time I saw him it would only be to rub my accomplishments in his face once I was the man I planned on becoming.

Although it hadn't become reality, the vision was clear. After I got my six-figure job, nice home, good man, and my luxury car, I would go by his house displaying each of my incredible accomplishments and watch his jaw drop in disbelief.

I couldn't bring myself to go home, but I really didn't have many other options. With no job, and not too many resources as a struggling college student, I couldn't afford my own place and had no clue what I was going to do at the rapidly approaching end of the semester.

"Don't worry too much about it. You'll think of somethin'. But one thing I won't let you do is go back home. I want you here with me. You're not safe there, and I'm not lettin' my baby go there without me to protect him," Dorey said.

He could sense my frustration and was trying to find the words to make me feel better about the situation. The truth was, my worry was justified, because with less than two weeks remaining to make such a critical move, time for thinking was over. It was time for finalizing plans, not brainstorming.

Dorey's cell phone rang. After clearing his throat, he answered it. Then after a very brief, professional-sounding conversation where he tried his best to hide his country accent, he said, "thank you" and hung up smiling.

"What was that about?" I asked, not used to hearing Dorey sounding so professional. Every other time I heard him on his cell phone, I knew he was talking to either one of his friends or relatives, and the conversations were never short or business like.

"Oh, nothing," he replied nonchalantly. "Just some lady from the athletics department callin' to tell me about the track scholarship information and application deadline for next year," he continued.

"Oh."

"I want you to go somewhere with me real quick," Dorey said, changing the topic abruptly.

"Okay, and where are we going?" I asked.

"One of my cousins wants me to come and help her move some furniture at her house. I figure two men will be bettah than just one and together we can get it done in half the time it would take me to do it by myself. Besides, my cousin is a talker, so if she goes into one of her long, drawn out stories I can just use you as my excuse to leave and tell her you have somewhere important to be," he said.

"How do you figure that you can just take me along and use me? First you want me for my muscles, and then you want to use me as a secret weapon not to listen to your cousin's tangents," I said jokingly.

"I can, and I will. Because you love me so damn much," he said, giving me a kiss and lifting me from my comfort zone on the bed. "Now get ready so we can go."

The car ride was short, just long enough to hear a few songs on the radio as we drove through the city with the windows down, feeling the breeze on an almost perfectly cloudless, sunny day.

Dorey took my hand in his while the other hand was on the steering wheel. Then he pretended to sing to me. Even though he couldn't sing on key if the world was depending on him, it was cute. The little things that most people failed to do were everyday occurrences for Dorey and that made it impossible not to love him.

Yes, by that point I loved Dorey, and with each passing day I was taking small steps toward the giant leap of falling in love. The simple things he did also helped keep things interesting and fun, and he always made me feel like I was special.

I looked admiringly at the apartment complex as we pulled up to the front access gate. The apartments looked like old Southern, colonial-style mansions on the outside, built with light colored bricks. Four huge, white columns and huge, arched windows towered atop the main entrances.

The name of the apartment complex was *Fountain Lake*. Just like the sign, directly behind it was a lake with a fountain. The lake held my attention for a moment as the fountain continually shot water straight up into the air and gravity brought it back to its starting place.

As the gate opened and we proceeded to drive slowly through the complex, it was like a whole new world was being unraveled. I was fascinated by my surroundings while getting my first taste of suburban life. Previously, my time was spent in the city of Atlanta, which undoubtedly had lots to offer, but this unseen area just outside the city had its own unique appeal. It was a beautiful contrast to dorm life at Clark.

The landscaping was full of rolling hills with neatly manicured lawns, shrubs, plants and flowers of all colors. Birds were flying overhead. I saw a few squirrels and my first chipmunk as it darted across the grass. There was even a family of ducks that looked like they were making their way to the lake in a single-line formation. It was quiet and peaceful, which stood out the most. For a moment it felt as if we had driven right past reality and ended up in the middle of some Walt Disney movie.

"Your cousin is living pretty good I see. How old is she?" I asked.

"She's our age," he said, as we pulled into a parking space in front of one of the beautiful buildings.

I thought about how nice it must be to come from money as I trailed Dorey into the building. His family was full of people who threw around money like it was going out of style. With my current financial status, I couldn't fathom living like this.

We climbed a spiral staircase to the top floor, and then walked down a hallway filled with doors adorned with gold-plated numbers.

Dorey knocked at the door, but there was no response. He knocked again, but there was still no answer.

Dorey then took out a set of keys from his pocket and unlocked the door.

"She gave you a set of keys?" I asked, wondering why he hadn't used them three knocks ago.

"You sure do ask a lot of questions," Dorey said sarcastically.

Once in the apartment I quickly noticed it was still and void, like it had already been vacated.

"Looks like someone else beat us to the moving," I said, trying to sound as sympathetic as possible. It looked like the apartment had been robbed, stripped bare of all its contents, leaving nothing, not even to the imagination.

"Your cousin sure is going to be pissed off when she finds out what's happened. You should call her and let her know so she can call the police or something. Imagine that, someone getting robbed in a neighborhood like this."

Dorey just stood there with a big smile, which soon turned into laughter as I rambled on and on about how the apartment had been burglarized. There was no humor in the situation, so why did Dorey seem so amused?

"Why are you laughing?"

"Here, hold these, baby," Dorey said, handing me the keys.

"Why are you giving me these?"

"Surprise, baby!" he said enthusiastically.

"Huh?"

I was still trying to process Dorey's offbeat actions.

"This is *our* new apartment. I made up the story about my cousin just to throw you off so that you would be surprised when you got here," he said smiling brightly.

He'd got the apartment so we could continue to be together through the summer after seeing my immobile frustration after being vexed over what I was going to do for the summer. This was the perfect solution, but I never would have expected anything like it. Dorey had been planning this surprise for weeks without my knowledge and was able to keep it a secret.

The call earlier about his supposed track scholarship was really a representative from Fountain Lake's leasing office telling Dorey that all the paperwork was processed, he was approved and could move in.

That was the kindest, sweetest, most generous thing anybody had ever done for me. The good news had me overcome with emotion as I made my way around our new, one-bedroom apartment. Walking from the living room, to the den, to the kitchen, to the bedroom and bathroom, I tried to digest the overwhelming event. It was just short of believable that someone cared about me enough to do something so wonderful.

"Okay, let's celibrate. Then I'll be off to look for a job so I can help pay for it," I said, as I started to undress Dorey, preparing to give him the best round of lovemaking he had ever and would ever receive.

As I kissed him, he looked into my eyes and said, "No. Guess what's next?" What's next? I wondered. Could there possibly be more?

"Next we have to go to the bank and get a joint account. That way, every time we get some money we can put a little bit into *our* account so that we can pay the bills on this place. I'm going to let you keep track of the bills. There will always be enough in the account to do it. Since we are doing the living together thing now, I just think that…"

I cut him off by kissing him so hard that I stole the words from his mouth. This man should be cloned I thought, so that I would never have to hear the saying "a good man is hard to find" ever again. I had more than a good man, I had a great man, and I was thankful for him. While we kissed, I replayed Dorey saying *our* in the back of my mind, which fueled a smile. I loved the way *our* sounded.

7

I ran with time at a feverish pace and when I finally stopped to rest, two years had past. Dorey and I were still together, still sharing an apartment, and I found myself experiencing something I thought was nonexistent,: a long-term relationship filled with love.

Some say love can make you do things you never thought you would. Whether it was because of love, Dorey or a mixture of the two, somewhere along my journey with them I discovered the true beauty of inspiration.

Dorey encouraged me to embark on a new venture using my creative writing skills. One day he'd come across some poems I wrote then after some minor ego stroking and persistence, he convinced me to try turning my love of writing into a career. I started compiling words and slowly those words turned into pages, enough pages to almost fill up a book. Soon, I would be giving poetry lovers all over the world something to watch out for.

Things between Dorey and I were going well, but the times weren't as carefree as our first year sharing a cramped dorm room on campus.

Living together in an apartment that we were solely responsible for brought new challenges and put weight on our shoulders. But the added pounds brought more spice to our already seasoned relationship. We hit highs and lows in those years that you never see in the Hollywood movies depicting perfect, fairytale stories. However, the years and trials we encountered brought resiliency, and though Dorey was far from perfect, there was no other man I could see myself loving. And on top of everything else, our times made for good writing.

Jarvis was the catalyst for our first altercation. Somewhere between my freshman and sophomore year he had become my second best friend. Jarvis and I had so many things in common that our friendship instantly became a seamless pairing from the start.

The way Dorey always seemed nonchalant when I would mention my best friend made me assume that he already knew the Jarvis I was referring to, which was also why I assumed he turned down every invitation we extended for him to hang out with us.

Most people might be a little iffy about being best friends with someone who had been with their mate sexually, but I was confident in the fact that what went on between Jarvis and Dorey was nothing.

Midway through his third semester in college, Jarvis dropped out of school after auditioning and being chosen to sing background for a well-known R&B artist who needed people for a six-month tour.

While out on the road with the band, we rarely spoke, which was abnormal for us. But as soon as he got back in town, it was like he'd never left. I threw him a surprise welcome home party at our apartment.

As Jarvis walked through the door and everyone shouted, "welcome back,", Jarvis wasn't the only one caught off guard. Dorey's mood shift was apparent as he suddenly realized that Jarvis was the same person who was a not-so-friendly reminder from his past.

All that time he claimed to not know who my best friend really was. Dorey said the reason he was so clueless was because he had tried his best to block that night from his memory and never knew Jarvis' real name. He'd met him as simply "J."

Dorey became furious and did everything just short of demanding me to dissolve my friendship with Jarvis. Even though I loved Dorey so much that at times I thought I would burst from all the feelings I had for him, there was just no way I could see myself throwing away the strong friendship I had built with my other best friend. Jarvis had become like a brother. I knew if Dorey's love was true, he wouldn't stick by that ultimatum and was certain we would work through that issue. It took a while for Dorey to move all the way past what he admitted to as his own embarrassment, but he eventually came around.

With all the highs and lows in our relationship, I was proudest of the fact that since Dorey and I had been together, his health was better than ever. I made sure to stay on top of him, making him take every pill prescribed- on schedule, go to every checkup, feeding him healthier foods, and trying to keep his stress at a minimum, so that he could stay healthy. He was now back in remission and had been for some time. If I had things my way, I would make sure he and cancer never corresponded again.

The piercing ring of the telephone cut through a dream during a much-needed and very restful nap. Protesting the fact that I was awake, I leisurely rolled my body over and quieted the annoyance by answering it.

After a very bass-filled, groggy, and somewhat annoyed sounding "hello", I regretted not letting the voice-mail take the call after hearing Dorey's baby's mother, Shawnquetta, on the other end.

Lately, she had been calling our apartment more than ever. From all the unwanted calls, I thought we were about to need a private hotline number installed just for her. She called about anything and everything that she could think of, trying to make it seem like it was concerning their daughter, but mostly it was to try and get money from Dorey.

Ever since the day we were first introduced, I didn't like her, but always remained cordial. I was never really sure why I didn't like her, but something about her didn't sit well with me. Maybe it was the fact that she had been with Dorey and I was a little jealous because they would have a bond for life through their daughter. Maybe it was because her calls were so frequent and unwanted. Maybe it was because Dorey seemed to get in a bad mood every time she came around. Maybe it was just because she was so loud and tacky.

How could she think it was okay to walk out of the house looking the way she did, and why didn't she have good friends to tell her otherwise? Each time I saw her, her clothes were shorter, tighter, and more low-cut, neglecting the fact she never lost the baby weight gained from her pregnancy. She always wore new clothes, new shoes, had her nails freshly manicured in vibrant hues, and had a new color weave plastered on top of her head at least once a week. It didn't take someone with Einstein's intellect to figure out that she was taking the money Dorey would give her for his daughter and spending it on herself, because she never worked a job more than two straight months.

Few and far between were the times that I saw Jasmine all cleaned up and looking nice. More often than not, when Jasmine came over to our apartment, she was in the same plain outfit, while her mother was all fancy and colorful, like some kind of genetically altered, ugly, country peacock.

Although the fact that Dorey was being used was apparent, I never brought up that obvious fact because there was no need. Deep down, he knew it too. He knew he was being used, but the fact that he loved his daughter so much shadowed that sad truth. The glow that transfixed him every time Jasmine was in his arms canceled out any amount of money Shawnquetta could ever squander.

Each weekend he shared with his daughter I silently watched in the background as everything else in Dorey's life became a non-issue and Jasmine was his number one priority. He loved that little girl so much that it was miraculous seeing so much love come from one man, making me love him even more. If Shawnquetta could only love her daughter with a fraction of the love Dorey gave to Jasmine, she could go from being a deadbeat hoochie momma to mother of the year.

Another thing I just couldn't stand about Shawnquetta was the way she looked at and interacted with Dorey. I'm not sure how she felt about me, but then again it really didn't matter. Whether she liked me or secretly shared the same contempt I had for her, she always treated me with as much respect as you could expect coming from someone who was as uncouth as she.

There were so many times that I wanted to tell Shawnquetta the truth about my relationship with Dorey, just to see her jaw drop. She thought Dorey and I were just boys sharing an apartment to save money. She had no clue that we were actually lovers. She never came past the living room of our apartment, so she was also clueless to the fact that there was only one bedroom.

It was so amusing to me that it had been almost three years that Dorey and I had been dating, and Shawnquetta, along with most people, were completely oblivious to us being anything more than just friends.

"Is Dorey there?" Shawnquetta's voice came shrieking through the phone.
"Yeah, hold on," I said.

Dorey was in the kitchen cooking when I entered, bringing him the phone. I gave him a long lingering kiss, intentionally taking my time so that Shawnquetta would have to hold.

"Thanks," Dorey said smiling after we were through kissing.

By that time it was around 1:20 and I had just enough time to put on my shoes, brush my teeth and head to class in order to make it on time. Dorey was still on the phone with Shawnquetta and seemed frustrated, so I left out without saying anything.

The mouthwatering aroma of home cooking attacked my nostrils when I got home from a long day of classes and my part time job that evening. Dorey had the table set and it was full of food that looked even better than it smelled. Smothered pork chops,; golden, yellow, sweet cornbread; creamy macaroni and cheese,; piping hot corn on the cob and mustard greens. Everything looked delicious.

Pausing for a moment before making my plate, I just stood there looking at the inviting feast. Just then, Dorey came from behind and started kissing me softly on my neck. He took his arms and wrapped them around my body, and then started hugging me tightly as if he hadn't seen me in years. His kiss was so soothing that I could slowly feel the tension I had been storing inside all day melt away from my body and disappear into a pool of nothingness on the floor below.

"Are you more hungry or more horny?" Dorey whispered seductively in my ear.

My stomach was so empty that it was growling almost loud enough to answer Dorey's question. I hadn't eaten anything since lunch. But as I turned around to see my boyfriend standing there, wearing nothing but a sexy smirk, I forgot all about my empty belly. The sight of Dorey made me hungry for something else, an appetite food couldn't satisfy. Though tempting, the food would have to wait.

"Horny."

"Good. I thought you might say that," Dorey said.

He began to peel away the layers of my clothing, stripping each article until skin was the only thing draping my body.

We began to make hot and intense love right there on the kitchen floor. Dorey was no doubt a good lover. He was all about pleasing me and as he lowered my body to the floor that night and started pleasing me just the way I wanted and needed to be, all I could do was moan with passionate professions of pleasure.

He started by kissing my face slowly and seductively, making his way down my body, paying special attention to all of the most sensitive spots he had discovered during our years together. His hands were moving simultaneously over my body, while his lips made me quiver.

"Turn over," he said.

At his command, I rolled over onto my stomach as Dorey began kissing and slowly licking from my neck down to the small of my back, blowing cool air softly across my skin, prompting me to squirm and the tiny hairs on my body to stand on end.

Then, he took his hands and firmly grabbed one side of my ass in each, parting my skin, totally exposing the center to the warmth of his kiss and tongue when he licked deep inside. The heat and rigidness of his tongue further aided in my relaxation. Uncontrollably, I went from a soft moan to a shout, letting him know I enjoyed everything his tongue was doing.

Right then in the midst of everything going on, the phone rang, slicing the mood in half and catching us completely by surprise.

"What the fuck!" I said, upset at the fact that the phone had to ring now, of all times.

"Come on, baby," Dorey whispered in my ear.

Trying hard not to let the phone completely ruin the mood, Dorey placed my naked body in front of his and we walked around the apartment, turning off every ringer on every phone so we would be sure to have no further interruptions.

As we made our way into the bedroom, Dorey placed a single finger in my mouth and I began to suck it with all the passion I was feeling inside. As he moved his finger around the inside of my mouth, he moaned softly in my ear.

Within a moment of removing his finger from my mouth, he placed it inside of me, making us both even more excited, as his finger slid further into me, slowly and with the delicacy of a well-trained artist.

When Dorey began to place himself inside of the walls he had just finished lubricating with his magical tongue, I felt like my body was going to buckle and explode from the inside outward.

The sex quickly grew intense, turning from slow and gentle as he found his place inside of me, to full-throttled, shit-talking, ass-slapping, heart-racing sex.

This occasional, freaky, no-holds-barred sex was always a treat. Sometimes we made beautiful, sweet love, and sometimes when we were short on time, we snuck in a quickie. Then other times, like tonight, we would fuck, raunchy and raw.

He was grabbing me so tight around my waist that I could feel the gentle burn of his hands and see my flesh turning red, but I didn't mind.

I placed my hands on the back of his neck with equal strength, as we looked into each others' eyes, confessing through loud grunts and various four letter words how much we were enjoying the moment. By the sounds of us, I could tell he was enjoying me as much as I enjoyed him.

"Say my name."

Dorey grabbed my legs and spread them as he pounded himself on top of me, going deep inside. I threw my body back at him, watching closely as he started to loose control. It was getting so good to him that he was growing weak.

He fell softly onto his back, pulling me up at the same time in one motion to let me get on top so I could take control. As I moved up and down on Dorey's engorgement, he started slapping me on the ass, and then rubbing his hands softly over the same area he just attacked.

While riding, my dominance turned us on even more. After a few minutes of being on top, I clenched myself tighter still around him and continued to ride, watching him lose focus and moan my name. While on top with his dick tightly gripped inside of me, I could feel it quiver just like his body had begun to do. I knew he was really close and so was I.

It had been about 45 minutes of non-stop sex and we could take no more. Every part of our bodies began to give way to ecstasy, and soon after, we came together, amazed at the huge amount of liquid we made on our new sheets before collapsing in each other's arms.

After Dorey and I finished eating, we went to take a shower together and ended going at it again under the warm, flowing water. After round two, we passed out on the bed, drained after another bout of some good, hot sex that had us in a love TKO.

Lying in his arms completely worn out, I was ready to fall asleep at any moment. I looked around puzzled because there in the room was the voice of someone else.

Dorey and I looked at each other for a moment, trying to figure out where the sound was originating. It was very low, but after just a few more seconds I knew exactly who it was. That voice I would recognize anywhere and under any circumstance.

It was Shawnquetta, but I knew she couldn't be in our home. She didn't have a key, and no one could have let her in. So where was her voice coming from?

I got up from my side of the bed and went over to Dorey. He was on the opposite side, looking down at the floor, worry filling every inch of his face.

"What's wrong?" I asked as I followed his eyes down to the spot capturing his attention and instantly realized what had him so troubled.

There on the floor was the phone that had been sitting on the nightstand. Somewhere between positions, Dorey and I must have knocked the phone off its base, and guessing by the voice of Shawnquetta coming through the line, I could tell that she had heard too much.

This wasn't going to be a good situation.

8

"You can have your faggot ex-boyfriend back! Ooops, my fault, what I meant to say was he's *all yours now*, and we don't have to share him no mo'!"

"What!" I demanded. "Who the hell is this?" I already knew who it was and already knew where this conversation was going. I just wasn't ready for the drama that was fated to come so early in the morning.

It had been a couple of weeks since Shawnquetta had overheard Dorey and I having sex and I was almost at the point where I thought we were off the hook.

"This is Shawnquetta, and I'm just calling to let you know that I found out about the little secret, homosexual affair you and Dorey been having behind my back. I must admit, job well done on the whole secretive, quiet-is-kept tip, but like my momma say, what is done in the dark will sho nuff come to light and the light is shining brightly now on you two homos."

"Shawnquetta, what the hell are you talking about?"

"I heard what y'all was doing the other night. Yeah, I heard it all, the 'ooh's' the 'aah's' and the 'say my names,',so don't even be trying to deny it. This whole time I thought you and Dorey were just friends. The *last* thing I expected to find out was that..."

"Shawnquetta, you make it seem like what Dorey does is any of your business. Yes, he is the father of your child, but other than that, you two don't have anything. You do your thing and he does his," I said.

"Oh, is that so, Mr. *College* man? Well, I see I'm not the only one who don't know about Dorey's *secrets*."

"What are you talking about?" I asked.

"Listen, is Dorey there? We need to talk."

"No, he isn't. Why don't you call his cell phone if it's that urgent? Oh yeah, that's right. I forgot he never gave you the number because he *doesn't* want you to have it," I said as condescendingly as I could.

Suddenly, there was this urge to tell her all the things Dorey had told me about their relationship, but I quickly decideed against it. She was no friend of mine, so why should I do her the favor of letting her know her ex always talked about her as if she was less than defecation?

But what did she mean by Dorey's secrets? Was she just rambling, the way she often could, or did she actually have some valid information that I was oblivious to?

Becoming more enraged with each passing second, I thought it best to try and end the phone call.

"Listen," I interrupted before she could continue for another second. "Good for you Shawnquetta. You really deserve a prize for being smart enough after all these years to finally find out that the father of your child is also my man. I wasn't aware that you learned detective skills in your GED class.

"There were so many times I wanted to tell you what was going on with us, but out of respect for Dorey's feelings, the ounce of respect that I *had* for you and the fact that it really wasn't any of your business, I didn't. However, all that aside, you will *not* call my home disrespecting me like this. Do you understand? Shawnquetta, I'm a grown-ass man, not a faggot, homo, sissy or any of the other names you may have used to describe me. And I'm damn sure not one of the ghetto friends you hang around with, so you won't treat me like one. What I do is my business, not yours. Trust me, you are the last person I need a lecture from about what I do in my personal life. Get your shit together before you come at me like that."

"But not…" Shawnquetta began.

"I wasn't finished!" I snapped. "And the next time you think of calling my home disrespecting me in the future, think again, because the next time, I will not be as nice." I hung up the phone before she had the time in her tiny brain to calculate a response.

The nerve of her, I thought, trying to calm myself after letting her successfully get me worked up. As I held out my hand I was so tense and frustrated it twitched involuntarily, revealing shot nerves.

Somehow she had found a spot under my skin. It was unbelievable that she actually had the audacity to try and call my home, insulting me the way she did, calling me names and preaching to me with those tired, old quotes "what you do in the dark will come to the light,", like she was the Messiah. I just knew she was going to use the most commonly used phrase of all about God making Adam and Eve not Adam and steve, but I hung up on her before she could.

How could someone on such a low level try to put me down? Shawnquetta, who sits around the house all day smoking marijuana, collecting welfare checks that my tax dollars help pay for, having no ambition, no job and no plans to do anything but keep her hair and nails "did" while her child goes neglected. Unbelievable!

Only a few moments had passed until the phone started ringing again. Reviewing the caller ID, I noticed that it was the same number Shawnquetta had just called from, so I let it ring.

After the fourth ring, my answering machine intercepted the call. Then, after only a few more seconds I heard the shrieking, high- pitched voice of my newly dubbed foe come blasting through the room, seemingly enraged and blurting out various obscenities.

"You bitch ass muthafukka! So you want be hanging up on me and then not be answering the phone when I know you're still there, fag? Well, listen to this! I'm sure you may not want to hear what I have to say, but I know there are a few other people that would just love to hear me. Dorey's mom and all his boys would just love to know that the two of you are a couple of *homosexuals*. And another thing, if you talk to Dorey before I do, which you probably will, tell him that he will *not* be seeing Jasmine anymore. I don't want my child hanging around any sissies."

Shawnquetta sparked an inferno in me with that second unwanted phone call. I grabbed the phone from the receiver and yelled into it with the low, husky, growl of a wild animal just before attack.

"Do what you have to do!" I said. "As a matter of fact, do you still live at the same place?"

"Yes!"

"Good. Stay there, 'cause I'll be over in a minute." I hung up just as I had moments earlier.

She made me furious enough that I planned on doing something I had never thought of in my whole life and something my mother told me never to do: fight a woman. She was wrong for calling me with such child-like pettiness. She was also out of line for the way she went about it. There are better ways of confronting someone and surely she could have found an alternative. I would have been a whole lot less pissed if she came to me as an adult and explained what was going on like a grown up instead of throwing around insults and talking down to me as if she were in some way superior.

Furthermore, she brought Dorey's daughter into the situation. If I wasn't sure about anything else, I knew Dorey loved his daughter with everything he had. He would do anything he could for her, never hurt her or let her be hurt. If Shawnquetta was serious about Dorey never seeing Jasmine, that would kill him, and I couldn't let that happen.

I knew I was wrong for hanging up on her, cursing and reducing myself, stooping to her ghetto level, but I knew that sometimes certain people just don't get it until you put things in a language they will understand. Shawnquetta was one of those people. She was the type that in order for her to comprehend, you would have to break things down to her in her native tongue, *chicken-head*.

I headed out of my apartment with an extreme case of tunnel vision, making my way to the parking lot. All I could see was me pulling up to Shawnquetta's house and handing her a good old-fashioned ass whoopin' sandwich, served up fresh on a silver platter. Afterward, I would pick up Dorey and take him downtown to the courthouse to file a motion for him to have full custody of Jasmine. I would find everyone I could to vouch for the fact that Shawnquetta was an unfit mother and make her regret ever crossing me.

When I got to my car, I started to feel idiotic.

"Where are you going?" I heard a familiar voice say to me as I stood at my car door. It was Dorey.

"What's wrong?" he asked, the flames in my eyes clearly revealed trouble.

"We have a problem," I said.

"What happened?"

"Shawnquetta called," was all I could say. In my anger, I didn't want to retell the whole story. I couldn't be the one to tell Dorey what she said about him not being able to see his daughter.

"What happened?" he asked again, rubbing the back of my head.

"You have to call her."

"Come on," he said, taking me by the hand and walking with me into the apartment.

At times, I felt Dorey knew me better than I knew myself. He knew what I was up to and taking me back in the house, was his way of keeping me from doing anything stupid.

When we got into the apartment, my head was spinning. Dorey went to the phone to call Shawnquetta, and I went to get something for my increasing headache. I then went to our bedroom and stretched across the bed, wishing all the chaos would go away.

I must have been exceptionally tired, because when I woke, it was one o'clock in the morning. I had slept all day. When I looked over to Dorey's side of the bed, expecting to see him sound asleep, he wasn't there.

The house was dark and motionless until the sound of my voice calling out Dorey's name echoed throughout it. There was no answer and silence resumed. It wasn't like Dorey to disappear in the middle of the night without saying anything, so I decided to dial his cell phone to find out where he was.

As if I hadn't already received my fill of her earlier, Shawnquetta's annoying voice boomed in my ear as soon as I picked up the phone. Dorey was on the line talking to her. They couldn't still be carrying on the conversation from earlier, I thought, and I started to put the receiver back on the hook. But before releasing myself from the line, I heard something that made me continue as a silent third person on the call.

Maybe I was still only partially coherent, because as I remained on the line, the conversation sounded too outrageous to be real. This was no dream, but I had to be sure I heard her right. This had to be some type of error, either that or there was some enlightening explanation forthcoming, which would clear up the shocking accusation I just heard. I was going to continue eavesdropping until I got the clarity I craved.

"So nigga, what you gonna do about this? Don't just be getting quiet!!" Shawnquetta demanded.

The line became still for a few moments until Dorey confirmed my fearful and unwanted suspicions. I still couldn't believe what I was hearing. How could this be?

"What about an abortion?' Dorey asked quietly, pain soaking his voice.

"Abortion? Nigga, please," Shawnquetta said. "I don't do abortions! If that was the case, I would have never had Jasmine. Hell, I was only seventeen and definitely didn't know nothing about babies. I'll be keeping this baby, just like I kept the last one, so get ready to be a daddy for the second time."

Dorey made his way back into our bedroom seconds later. There I was with the light on, waiting for him on the bed with a raised eyebrow and an unmovable look of disgust. I was still in shock from the bombshell that had just been dropped. There was no one solid emotion I felt, just a patchwork quilt of many different sentiments that I used to wrap myself in until I was sure of which to follow. I felt stunned, dejected, betrayed, hurt, mad, fearful, and that was just to name a few.

Rage came over me when our eyes met. The phone was still in my hand and tears started to puff up and cool my fiery face as they fell. I stared down at the phone in disbelief.

Dorey stood, frozen and speechless. He knew he was caught. He offered no explanation, no apology, nothing! But then again, an explanation wasn't necessary and an apology wouldn't be anywhere near sufficient.

I threw the phone, hitting Dorey in the center of his chest and still he stood in silence. I could feel myself growing more upset with each passing second. The very sight of him was too much, and I wanted nothing more than for him to be on the opposite end of the earth, far away from me.

With all the hostility that had been building and all my might, I charged toward Dorey and started swinging my fists. A trance-like state shackled me, and all I kept thinking was that I had to hurt him for hurting me. Thoughts of him and Shawnquetta began to mock me. I felt foolish, because I would have never believed something like this could happen had I not heard it for myself.

Dorey did his best to keep me off of him, but it was no use. I was possessed with anger. At that moment it probably would have taken three or four people to hold me back.

Surprisingly, I had gone my whole life without any physical altercations except the ones with my father. I thought about that fact in my anger, which added strength to my rage. How could the only two men I loved hurt me so badly?

The love I felt for Dorey was intense. I loved him because he made me feel lovable and worthy of happiness. But at that moment, my love for him lay dormant beneath frustration. My feelings couldn't be described in words, only punches.

Dorey kept trying to calm me down, grabbing my arms and trying to hold them.

"Baby, relax!" he yelled repeatedly.

I couldn't hear anything he said. I just kept swinging. Soon I began to feel more than just arms trying to hold me. Fists that were not my own found themselves on my body and things went from a one-man battle with Dorey trying to calm me, to a two-man, war.

"No this bastard didn't have the nerve to be fighting back!" I thought to myself. I had done absolutely nothing wrong. Unless devoting myself to our relationship over the past few years was a crime, then I was completely innocent, and the fact that he was now hitting me ignited my rage to dangerous levels.

With a strong and forceful push, Dorey attempted to free himself. Instantly, something took over me and I turned into a crazed lunatic.

The scariest part of our battle was when I looked at Dorey and swore I could see the eyes of my father, the same disapproving, evil eyes I saw the night when he and I had our first fight years ago.

I went charging after Dorey once more as if he really was the man whose seed helped create me. I took out all of the stored aggression that had been mounting ever since the night he beat my body into a bloody fraction of its former self and left me scarred for life.

Seeing my father in Dorey freaked me out. Then, I realized temporary insanity was not just something trumped up in court cases to gain the sympathy of a judge and jury. It was real, because I had gone mad in that moment.

Dorey came to me and reached out, pulling me close. Meanwhile, I was still throwing unbridled punches like something from a video game. Somehow we ended up in the kitchen, the very same place where we had recently made love.

"Calm down!" he demanded. "Just calm down and let's talk about this!"

"What is there to talk about?" I snapped. "Do you want to explain why you went out tipping behind my back with Shawnquetta? Or about how you got her pregnant for the second time? Well, playboy, I don't want your explanation, so save it!"

"So it's like that?" he asked, seeming surprised by the fact that I didn't want to talk.

"Hell yeah, it's like that!" I came charging toward Dorey, yelling, "HOW COULD YOU!"

My rage resumed.

This time he was prepared. He saw me coming and took off running. Though our apartment was a nice size, there weren't many places he could go to escape my wrath.

I followed after him as he bolted into the bedroom, grabbed the phone from the spot on the ground it had fallen earlier when it hit him, went into the bathroom and shut the door, locking it behind him so I could not get in.

As I stood there by the bathroom door, I wondered what was wrong with me. This was the man I loved, so why were we hurting each other like this? Yes, he hurt me and I was upset, but I never imagined putting my hands on Dorey in any other way but lovingly.

Listening at the bathroom door, I heard him as he dialed numbers on the phone. After a few seconds passed, his voice echoed off the walls of the bathroom, explaining to the party on the other end that he needed help.

"I need someone at 3650 Ashford Dunwoody Road, apartment *204,* quick!" he said.

He was in there calling the police on me. I couldn't believe it, but I sure wasn't going to stick around the apartment until it sunk in, with flashing lights and a set of silver handcuffs around my wrists.

"You pussy! Why did you have to call the cops like a little bitch?" I said, pounding on the door with sore fists.

Dorey didn't say a word and the whole apartment suddenly grew deafeningly quiet.

Reality hit me when I looked into the mirror on the wall of the powder room outside the bathroom. Blood was streaming from my nose. What was happening to us?

Fearful of what may have happened if I stayed, I grabbed my keys and left. I got in my car and just started driving.

I drove with no destination or intentions other than to clear my head, to get away from Dorey and all the pain I was feeling. I just drove and drove and drove until my head started to free some of the pain it had been harboring.

I ended up on the side of the highway, broken into so many pieces and with so many tears filling my eyes that I could no longer contain my emotions well enough to drive. As long as I live, that day will forever be stitched in my mind as the day I lost my faith in men, relationships and love.

9

Shook by love's first broken heart, I sat dazed and confused, trying to sort out all of the demons in my head the best way I knew how. It was exactly one month after I had broken up with Dorey and this particular evening had me feeling exceptionally lonely.

Broken , I just couldn't summon the inner strength to complete a task that was once so easy. There before me stood a full-length mirror that shined like a spotlight, highlighting how disastrously wrong my life had become. My distorted reflection revealed some sort of strange monster that had previously gone unnoticed. Somewhere along the line, this creature started emerging and slowly took shape, until the finished product stood in my place, making me doubt everything about myself. What was this image in the mirror staring back at me that I couldn't bare to look at without bowing my head in shame?

"Mirror, Mirror on the wall, when in turmoil who can I call?" I asked as my sad reflection stood clueless and silent.

The scenario may have been a little different. I was older and in another state, but there I was, back at square one, asking for help from the man in the mirror, just as I had years ago.

When life dealt me a hand full of adversity, it always seemed to bring out the worst in me. But there in my current bout of depression, "the worst of me" couldn't even adequately describe who I'd become.

The outside of me was in shambles, unkempt, ashamed and clearly in need of restoration. On the inside things weren't any better.

Foreign voices filled my head, making it hard to think about anything other than the pain I felt. My esteem, integrity, and overall way of life were all challenged by the inner voices, which articulated effortless expressions slicing through my already broken heart. At that moment, I was feeling like there was no worse person in the world to be other than me, and it was becoming way too much to bare.

"This is exactly what you get for living such a sinful lifestyle. Your parents told you that living this way would only bring you down and now look at you. What the hell made you think you could make a relationship with another man work? Do you not believe that there is a special spot in hell for people like you?"

This barrage of insults was a culmination of all the doubts I'd tried to escape for years, manifested and unleashed all at once.

"SHUT UP!" I yelled, but to no avail. By the time the sound of my words faded, the attack of my subconscious reconvened.

Without anywhere else to go, Jarvis graciously offered to let me stay with him for a while. At first I was in denial, thinking my relationship with Dorey would soon change for the best, but a month had passed, and with each day my hopes for reconciling gradually faded.

Life seemed as unnerving as a recurring nightmare. I wanted to awaken to life the way it was, back when my ignorance equaled bliss.

There was this vegetated state imprisoning me since leaving Dorey. Most days I wouldn't even get out of the bed.

Trying to find some sense of solace in the satin sheets, I would pull them up over my head, tuning out the world as I lay trying to cope.

Earlier that day, I got a call from my academic advisor telling me that since I had been missing so many classes lately, my grades had suffered so much that I would be incapable of passing anything that semester. Under normal circumstances that news would have stung, but then again, if things were normal it wouldn't have happened. The only reason I missed those classes was because things were so terribly abnormal. The pain of losing Dorey was greater than the revocation of my scholarship, which was about to happen.

I longed for the comfort of Dorey's touch; wanting to make love to him just one more time and lay together until the morning. I wished that he would kiss me, hug me, and tell me that after everything we had been through he was still in love with me and everything was going to be okay. But he wasn't around, so I decided to seek comfort in another way.

Before tonight, the only time I'd been drunk was on my 21st birthday. When I officially crossed over into adulthood, I went out and got so full of liquor to celebrate that the repercussions resulting in the morning after's hangover was enough to make alcohol never appeal to me again. There in Jarvis' apartment at his kitchen table with a row of bottles filled with all different types of liquor, a few crystal glasses with ice and some orange juice to mix my pleasures. I was about to revisit a world called inebriation.

Somehow everything that was once right in my life all of a sudden was snatched right up from under me and it sent me crashing down to the ground and flat on my face. Although I was alone, I felt the whole world could see my failure. My man, my good grades, my scholarship and my happiness were all being snatched away one by one.

I said a prayer as tears began to fall. I prayed for God to see me through my situation and prayed for a miracle, because that's what I was feeling it would take for me to survive the rut trapping me. The prayer did little to silence the storm going on in my head. A million thoughts racing at the speed of sound left me feeling like a mad man without hope for any resolve.

The phone rang, further setting off my already uneasy nerves. I made my way to it without even looking at the caller ID. I switched the ringer to the off position and returned to the kitchen, cut off the lights, sat down to the table, and began to pour my first drink.

Right around the time I finished my second beverage, the treacherous thoughts that had enveloped my mind started to subside. It almost felt like I was thinking clearly for the first time since leaving Dorey. I liked this feeling so I kept the drinks flowing.

"One bad man in my life being replaced by another," I said to myself, slurring words as I struggled to lift the glass full of the golden brown Jack Daniels whisky and ice to my lips. The liquor no longer burned my throat as it traveled down my insides, because my body had gone numb.

Soon I lost track of how many glasses of alcohol I'd consumed, not realizing that I had drank a whole fifth of vodka and was now halfway through the bottle of Jack.

I knew that mixing my liquors was not a good thing and my body would pay for it in the morning, but I really didn't care. The alcohol was the only thing bringing me even an ounce of comfort.

The book of poetry I had just finished before the breakup was in front of me. That same book filled with the inspiration of a "good" man and "good" relationship was challenging every bit of dignity I had. I felt so foolish for being blind to the fact that I was too in love to see that everything wasn't so "good." The book had to go! I went to the kitchen sink, ripped out every page, tearing the paper and poems into fractions, then lit the remains and watched the inferno steal away into black ash.

Something inside led me to grab a sheet of paper and a pen. I wanted to release myself, and writing had always been a great outlet. When I wrote, I was free. I could go to other worlds and be whoever I wanted to be. Maybe if I were able to write down some of the thoughts going through my mind, it would bring clarity and peace--or at least take me away from the last few lingering feelings of pain.

I took the pen in my hand, barely able to keep its grasp in my liquored-up state. The writing didn't go well, but I continued, not stopping until I was unable to continue. The words were sloppy and blurred, mirroring my vision. The pen slipped from my hand at least once every few seconds. Each time a tear fell, the moisture from my eyes soaked into the paper, making the ink run together. I didn't even know what I was writing and couldn't read the words already released, but it didn't matter. It was temporarily taking my mind, so I kept on writing until the liquor completely intervened and I had lost all hand-eye coordination.

The numbness felt sinfully good, encouraging me to keep drinking, knowing that once sober I would return to a painful reality. As I made my way slowly through the bottles lined up on the kitchen table, the room suddenly became hazy. My eyes grew heavy and the world started spinning around me before turning black.

When I awoke my best friend was at my side, but he was the only familiar vision. Scanning my surroundings, I noticed that everything looked strangely new. With blurred vision and eyelids that seemed to weigh a hundred pounds apiece, I continued to look around the room until I realized that I was not at the kitchen table anymore. I was in a hospital.

I tried to call out to Jarvis and ask him what was going on, but the words only came out in fragments. Each word felt like fire shooting out of my throat as I fought to force out a barely audible sentence.

"The nurse said your throat may feel a little sore because they had to intubate you," Jarvis said.

"What happened?" I asked.

Jarvis went on to tell me how he got worried after I hadn't picked up the phone the night before when he called from work. He said he had left an urgent message on the phone for me to call him a.s.a.p., and when I didn't, he knew something had to be wrong. He left work early only to find me passed out on the kitchen floor in a puddle of my own vomit and when he tried to wake me, I wouldn't respond so he called the ambulance. He also went on to tell me that the doctors said I had a terrible case of alcohol poisoning and there was a chance I could have died had I not received medical attention.

There were all kinds of cords and wires hooked up to my body, checking my vital signs and an IV was in my arm. I silently wished that I had died, because the pain I had been feeling last night before I had even taken my first drink was now heightened a hundred fold.

"Let me ask you something, Jay," Jarvis said.

"Okay."

"You are my best friend, right?"

"Jarvis, you know I am. Why are you asking me that?"

"And you know you can tell me anything, right?"

"Yeah."

"So why didn't you tell me you were going to try and kill yourself?"

"Huh? What are you talking about?"

Tears started to fall from Jarvis' eyes, which shocked me. That was the first time I saw Jarvis cry. He always appeared to be tough as nails, like I usually tried to be. His eyes were overflowing with tears as he retrieved a piece of paper from his pocket, unfolded it, and handed it to me.

"What's this?" I asked, as I started to read the paper. He didn't respond.

After only getting about two sentences into the barely legible note, my eyes started to water uncontrollably as well. The somewhat forgotten and chilling details of the previous night came rushing through my mind as I read.

The piece of paper I was holding contained the words of my broken heart, written as I was drinking. What appeared from the scattered words that I could make out was a suicide note.

Through the sloppy penmanship and smudged ink, I could still feel the same pain I felt at the time I had written it. I had actually forgotten about the note and along with it, most of the evening. I had no clue that I had written the things I was reading, things about how horrible my life was going and that maybe I would be better off dead.

I sobbed, realizing that the large amount of alcohol I consumed was an attempt to kill myself, something I never thought about, let alone thought I would have the courage to follow through with.

The look on my best friend's face as I looked into his eyes did the unimaginable. Seeing the disappointment on Jarvis' face made me feel even worse. He was trying his best to mask his emotions and be strong for me, but I could see right through his façade. I knew him far too well to be fooled by a front.

As I lay motionless, I decided I had to snap out of my funk. Now things were serious. Not only was I hurting myself, but I was also starting to hurt other people. I never even stopped to think about the pain my friends and family would have to endure if I had died, and why? Only because I was selfish and shallow enough to let a man break me down this way.

I hated the person this situation had made me become. Never in my life had I ever disappointed myself, but there I was, now looking disappointment in the face, and I knew something had to be done. The man I was, wasn't the real me, he was unwelcome and had to go.

Fighting back crocodile tears, I drove through Atlanta wondering what I was going to do with myself. I was a total wreck and cried oceans each and every time I thought about how much of a fool I was to have put so much love and devotion into one person, blindly assuming that he was doing the same for me.

Going on with my life was exceptionally difficult for a number of reasons. Number one: Dorey was my first. I had never given my all to anyone else, so when it came to being in love, he was all I knew. I thought we had something real. But now I was finally seeing the end of something I thought would be everlasting.

Even having the proof for myself, it was still just short of believable. I couldn't recount the numerous times over the last week alone that I thought I would wake up and this whole experience be reversed, but instead waking only to find a pillow full of tears and the pain that had rocked me to sleep the night before.

Everything I did, everywhere I went and almost everything I even thought about reminded me of Dorey. The apartment we had shared was full of our memories. The car I was driving we had made love in on numerous occasions. Even as I drove through the city, every corner of it seemed sadly familiar and brought back visions of happier times. The parks, restaurants, malls, stores and even the sky above reminded me of Dorey and how on our six-month anniversary he promised to do everything in his power to give me everything he could, just short of the moon.

I wanted to be like a bird, grow wings and fly away from the scene of my heartache, up to a higher ground where things would be different and I could have a new start or at least find peace of mind until the storm passed.

Many of the thoughts that periodically raced through my mind I knew couldn't be healthy, but there I was with my overwhelming emotions and no clear plan of how I was going sort through them.

The only thing I was sure of was that I had to escape, because the mildly psychotic thoughts I once shrugged off and convinced myself were too crazy to follow through with, suddenly weren't sounding so bad. If I continued to be surrounded by torment, I felt that either one of two outcomes would find me: being committed in a mental institution, or getting arrested for inflicting the pain I was feeling onto Dorey and Shawnquetta through violent means.

Since I felt an almost certain assurance that I would never grow wings and transform into a bird, I thought about what would be the next best option.

I decided to just drive until either there was no road left to travel, my pain subsided, or my body was too tired to drive any longer, whichever came first.

10

Sitting in fear and silence, I tried to figure out just where, just when, and just what had prompted the vicious trigger to be pulled, unleashing a fiery bullet into the core of my life, leaving it shattered in so many pieces that now it seemed unmendable.

Was it when Dorey cheated on me, or was it when I allowed myself to love him?

A couple of months ago I was on the verge of achieving greatness. I was in my senior year at one of Atlanta's most prestigious black universities, less than two semesters away from graduation, and soon to embark on the colorful future I had been painting in my mind ever since I left this very spot years ago.

With so much promise, so much potential and so much knowledge, why was I dumb enough to let such an obviously stupid thing happen?

Maybe it wasn't too late for me to turn it all around, I thought. But I knew in order to rebound; I would need a firm foundation in which I could begin to pick myself up from the dirty mess I'd made.

All out of options and depleted resources, I found myself right back at the very place I'd pegged as the point of no return. I wasn't supposed to be here.

Far from being in a position capable of gloating, I tried desperately to humble myself, preparing for the major groveling I would have to do and tried to build a barrier around my already shattered pride so that when it got danced on, I could stand strong.

Subconsciously, I led myself there because I knew I had no other choice. I had nowhere else to go and this inevitable fate was silently calling my name.

Basically, I was homeless. Technically, I had no place to call my home. The last week was spent in my car, drifting around town and trying to avoid this moment for as long as possible. With nowhere to shower and none of the comforts of home I'd taken for granted, I was starting to smell of lingering perspiration and various body odors which lay thick in the confines of my car.

The long journey, the uncertainty of how my life would eventually turn out, the earth-shattering events that led to my tattered existence, and living in filth and squalor all seemed easy compared to the task at hand. Somehow, some-way, I would have to face my tormentor once again and ask him, no, beg him for help. He would probably revel in the sight of me in such a broken state, find pleasure in my pain, tell me a half a million times that he told me so, and somehow find a way to make me feel even worse. So I just sat in the car stalling, trying to avoid lying in the bed I had made for as long as possible.

The sounds of my screams had me frozen. Was my mind playing tricks on me? It couldn't be real, but the sounds I heard of my voice yelling out at the top of my lungs for help sounded and felt as real as they did that night.

By walking in that door, I would have to relive all the pain, anguish and torture he once inflicted on me. With one look in his eyes I knew it would all come back to me and haunt my thoughts. Even in my dreams I would have to relive the pain. Unsure if I was strong enough to go back, I kept prolonging an unavoidable fate, but the sad reality was I would eventually have to surrender.

Over my life I can say that I've had to taste many things that weren't so pleasing on the palette, but on that day I had to digest a pill so jagged and bitter I thought I would never be able to swallow it. The taste of my shattered pride lay like a heavy, acid-soaked brick in the pit of my stomach as I stood at the door with my finger over the doorbell, trying to convince myself to make the final step.

"I was expecting you home any day now, and I guess my suspicions were right-as usual. Mr. Big, Mr. Bad. Or should I say Ms.? You left out of here with your ass on your shoulders, thinking that you were going to conquer the world. Now look at you, you look even worse than you did when you left. And what's that *fukkin-awful* smell?!" my father screamed as I walked into the house.

I stood there with my head bowed in shame. I knew this was the punishment I would have to face and I knew he wasn't going to make things easy.

"So you fucked up your grades and lost your scholarship? How long did you think you could keep that a secret? I guess you didn't know that your school sent us a letter telling us everything.

"So did you come back to get some money, because if that's what it is, you can forget it. I will not support a failure. I work hard for my money, and I won't just go throwing it away. I did that up until you were eighteen because that was my *job* as a father. Now you're a man and will have to support yourself."

By that time my mother overheard my father's cold words, coming to see what all the commotion was about and to whom he was talking. She looked astonished to see me standing there and quickly came over with a smile and a hug.

"Hi, Jayson. It's so good to see you!" she exclaimed

"Hi, Ma."

"Your daughter came home to ask for some money," my father said, continuing to spew his icy words.

"Now, Jonathan, don't you start that! I won't have you talking to Jayson that way," she said firmly, as I watched my father's eyes drift upward into his skull.

"No, Ma. I didn't come here for any money. I just… I need a place to stay until I get back on my feet. Things aren't going so well for me right now and I *need* a little help," I said.

"Oh, hell no! If you really think I would let your ungrateful, disrespectful ass move back into my house that *I* pay the bills for, you must really be out of your damn mind. *You* fucked up, not me, and not your mother, so I suggest you go back to whatever mess it is that you made down in Atlanta and *clean it up!* Maybe that will teach you what being a *real* man is all about. Since you are so bad, you should be able to handle that with no problem, right?" My father kept talking while I tried in vain to overlook the vengeance in his voice that ripped right through me.

As he stood there waiting on my answer, which I clearly was not going to give, my mother interjected, playing referee in what was turning into more of challenge than I had anticipated. I knew it would be hard, but I didn't know the struggle would be this difficult. I was almost about to do just as my father said and leave, heading back to Georgia or wherever I ended up. Anywhere seemed better than continuing to subject myself to his bullshit.

"Jonathan, you stop it right now! This is totally uncalled for. He is still our son, and I will not stand by and watch you treat him like this. Jayson, you can stay here for as long as you like. Go get your things and I will start getting your old bedroom ready for you," my mother said calmly.

"Baby, you may want to rethink your stance on this matter. Think about who you married and who you said your vows to. Think about who you've spent the last twenty-plus years with. And think about who *won't* be here if *he* stays, 'cause as long as *he's* in my house, I sure as hell won't be," my father demanded.

With that said, I headed to the car to get some of my things. As I was gathering my belongings, I watched as my father came storming out of the house, got into his car, and then sped off into the night.

My father's hateful actions caused the strong-wall I'd built to come crashing down, leaving me just moments from breaking. Why did our relationship have to be so strained? I needed him to be the loving, caring man that taught me how to ride a bike, change my oil, and was there to pick me up every time I fell when I was learning to walk. Even after he'd hurt me so bad for so long, and with no signs of remorse, I still longed for his love.

As my mother stood inches away looking helpless, my inherent ways surfaced. Whenever in pain, it was impossible for me not to lash out at the closest person and cast my hurt on them. However immature and selfish my slingshot emotions could sometimes be, they helped me deal with pain.

I said the first thing that came to mind that was sure to rub my mother the wrong way and start an argument. She was my ally at a time when I needed all the help I could get, so why was it so hard to keep my childish ways contained?

"Thanks Ma for being there for me for a change," I said with uncontrollable sarcasm.

"Jason, what the hell is that supposed to mean."

"Nothing," I yelled as I turned to walk away.

"Jayson! Don't you dare walk away from me like that when I'm talking to you."

"But Ma, there's nothing to talk about."

"Apparently there is. Judging from the comment you just made I'd say we have *a lot* to talk about."

It was the wrong time to be voicing my concerns and opening old wounds, but that didn't stop me from being irrational. I was out of control in every aspect of life and in misery I longed for company. My mother seemed like the best person to suffer in chaos with because she was usually so mild mannered and easily affected.

"You are just as bad as him sometimes. I'm surprised you didn't go chasing after him!"

"Jayson, you are talking real foolish right now."

"No, it's not foolish it's the truth. For the past four years you've been siding with him and treating me like I was worth less than dust in your life. The secret phone calls you had to make only when *he* wasn't around. The emails and letters that we had to keep private, because you knew if *he* found out *he* would treat you as bad as he's been treating me. I need a mother, not a hush-hush pen-pal."

"He is my husband…"

"And I am your son!"

"Jayson! You know that I love you and I want nothing but the best for you in your life. It's just hard to stand by and watch you make bad decisions and pretend that everything is okay. Yes, things have been different between us since finding out you are, gay, but how do you expect me to act…"

"You say you love me, well then show it. And it shouldn't be an *act*."

"I do show you love."

"How so? By the once in a blue moon phone calls that I get that are so rushed that there's barely a chance for a hello and goodbye?"

"You don't know the half of what I go through here with your father, and how many times I've come to your defense. I just don't agree with homosexuality. I think it's wrong, but that doesn't mean that I don't love you. What it does mean is that I'm praying for you and eagerly waiting for you to become the man that God would have you be."

"So the only way that I will be able to get a real relationship with my parents would be to change from being who I am, into who they want me to be? Since you want to bring religion into this conversation, doesn't being a Christian mean you're striving to be Christ like? And doesn't God give unconditional love? Well why cant you?"

My words fell so heavily on my mother that she was at a loss for words. I had become so worked up while discussing such a sensitive topic that my body was trembling and in need of rest.

"Now Ma, if you don't mind I just need some sleep. We can talk later when I'm feeling more level headed."

By the time I walked away, both of us had glassy eyes that were full of tears revealing so many unanswered questions and so much unspoken pain.

11

Things seemed to be bad on both ends, and my lot was uncompromising in its sovereignty. The road ahead seemed too rough to tread. Every day I stayed at home was a day that I was made to feel ashamed of who I was and guilty for my mother and father's strained relations.

I'd found that the struggles my parents were experienceing weren't purely my fault, but even still I knew I was adding extra tension. They had been dealing with their own issues before I came, I was just the good excuse my father needed to run away from his problems.

My mother and I had begun to bond like old times and I couldn't have been happier to be salvaging a relationship with her that I thought was doomed. She eventually shared with me without going into great detail that we were dealing with similar situations. I'd opened up to her about Dorey and she alluded to the fact of catching my father being unfaithful.

I knew I'd noticed a change in my mother. She was stronger and stood up for herself and me without just playing the passive homemaker role I was accustomed to seeing. My fathers' infidelity didn't seem to affect her as strongly as Dorey's did me. She seemed to be coping very well and seemed to have settled things. Either way the drama at home was too much for me at a time when I was searching for peace and my presence was only adding to the fiasco.

Suddenly I longed to be back in Atlanta.

While living in my parent's home, my ill- feelings toward Atlanta became less intense. Things weren't smooth terrain there, but at least there I was only responsible for messing up one life, my own. At home I felt responsible for messing everything up, my life and my parents', because they hadn't spoken a word to each other since the night I came home and my father was still M.I.A..

The life I had left in Atlanta was far from perfect. Actually, the life I had down there was the reason I had come crawling back home, practically begging to stay with my parents. But after only a week away, I had been able to put things into perspective. By talking to my mother, I was given a deeper insight. I learned that life is far from perfect and from time to time it will throw curveballs your way, filled with things you would never expect. But that's just life's way of making you strong and seeing if you're fit to live in an imperfect world.

I'd realized that when life drops you head first into adversity, the important thing is not to run away, but to deal with it head on, look adversity in the eye and conquer it. Then and only then will you be ready for the next trial that life brings your way.

With my new perspective and newfound strength, I decided I was ready to go back to the same place that had defeated me. Only this time I would emerge victorious, even if it killed me.

12

"Welcome to South Carolina" the highway sign read, letting me know that I was almost there as I inhaled a deep pull of fresh air. Though my body was stiff and tired after driving for 10 long hours, headed back to the very place I'd just left, it didn't matter, because it would soon be over.

As I looked around South Carolina's somewhat familiar landscape, I made a quick vow never to let my life get so bad that I would feel like I had to leave home again.

They say home is where your heart is, and even though I was not born and raised in Georgia, and my heart was broken there, in that same place was where my heart resided. There were so many memories there, and though they were mixed, good and bad, it was still good to almost be home.

"If I ever needed you before, it was nothing compared to the way I need you now," I said, after calling Jarvis on my cell phone.

"What's up?" he asked.

"I'm on my way back to Atlanta. You know what I was going through back in Pennsylvania, and I just couldn't take it. It was too much and I've decided that bad times in

Atlanta are better than bad times anywhere else. So to make a long story short, I know you let me stay with you before, but I really need to stay there now, just until I find somewhere else," I said, hoping he'd understand.

"Is that all you want? The way you sounded made me think you needed one of my kidneys or something. You know you can always stay with me. I don't know why your ass ever left in the first place. You could have saved a lot of time and gas money if you would have just stayed put."

"I know, but I just felt like I had to get away for a little while."

"With gas being as expensive as it is, you could have *gotten away* someplace closer. But anyways, I'm glad you're coming back. I missed your crazy ass!" Jarvis said.

"You act like we haven't been talking on the phone every day since last week."

"We have, but it's different when you're not here. So where are you now?"

"I just crossed the state line about five minutes ago when I called you."

"Good. That will give you about another hour or so before you get to my place. It's six o'clock now. That will put you here around sevenish, giving you just enough time to get halfway settled, and still more than enough time to get yourself ready for the club. Tonight is Thugged out Tuesday at Traxx, so you know it's gonna be nice. I'm so glad you're back and not a moment to soon. We have some catching up to do."

"Thank you so much. I really appreciate this."

"You know I'm always here for you."

I continued driving as Jarvis rambled about how glad he was that I was back.

I delicately juggled my focus between Jarvis and the highway, but the road began to need me more. There was a red Mustang darting in and out of the lanes. Road rage started to seep from my pours when the man behind the wheel of the Mustang cut in front of me abruptly, slamming on his brakes for the third time. His negligent driving made me mash my hand down firmly on the horn while it bellowed continually.

An earful of conversation and 30 minutes later, I arrived at Jarvis' apartment. He stayed on the phone, talking to me from the time I called until I was standing right in front of him in his apartment, not hanging up the phone until after we had hugged. After a brief hello, Jarvis continued where he had left off—incessantly talking, without taking a breath.

"I think I have some good news for you, but I'm not quite sure yet. I will keep you posted, but for now let's start by getting you unpacked. I know you have got to be tired. Did you drive straight through the whole way?"

"Yes, and I am tired as hell."

"Well then, you need to hurry up and put your things away, take a quick nap, and get yourself together. Don't forget we are going out tonight."

"Okay."

"I'm so glad you are back in a real city. I was worried that if you stayed back home too long you might *really* go crazy. I mean, what is there to do where you're from anyway? And what good has ever come out of Pennsylvania except Patti Labelle and cheese steak?"

"Shut up, fool. You've never even been to where I'm from, so what would you know about what we have and what we don't?"

"I never wanted to go there either. So what does *that* tell you?"

We both started laughing. Afterward, Jarvis helped me bring my things into the apartment and together we started to unpack.

We arrived at the club looking like a pair of Hollywood celebrities, dressed in brand new clothes and shoes purchased earlier that day.

The pulsating beat of the loud music escaping from inside the club to the street greeted us as we approached the VIP line and waited anxiously to get in.

Attractive men engulfed us from the moment we walked in the door. There were some not so attractive ones, too, but the sexy men had them outnumbered. Many faces were familiar; theirs were the faces of those who were regular fixtures around Atlanta's club scene. Along with the old were a few new faces scattered in the mix. I could spot the new meat from a mile away, because those where the men who had flocks around them just waiting to get a chance at a possible encounter with a "new kid on the block." Fresh faces always attracted the largest crowds, because most people prefer new things including mates.

Everyone was dressed up and parading around the club, with their best urban attire since it was Thugged out Tuesday. There was an overflow of men in wife beaters, baggy clothes, sweatbands and Timberland boots. They all put their best self on display in hopes of landing a date. Even the most effeminate men would make an attempt on Tuesday to leave the tight jeans at home and sport a more boyish look in order to keep up with the theme of the evening, even if by doing so most looked like fish out of water.

The majority of men were on the prowl, looking for nothing but sex. A few came out to dance, drink and have a good time. The rest had the hungry look of sexual famine in their eyes, wanting to go home with someone and have a quick fling that would hold them over until they came out again, only to repeat the same pattern.

We walked around the club, stopping every few seconds so that we could say "Hi" to one of Jarvis' many acquaintances. He knew a lot of people from going out, so every time we went out together, it was a must that we walked around and spoke to everyone before dancing, drinking or anything else.

"Well, well. Look who's back!"

I turned around and saw a vision that had me feeling like I was staring at a living apparition. All at once the wonderful vibe of the night came to a sudden, powerful halt. I couldn't believe he was standing there, smiling at me with his arms open wide. Did he actually expect a hug? From the look on his face he must have forgotten that he had not so long ago broken my heart.

"Dorey?" I said, shocked to see him. He had never been to a gay club the whole time we dated. Every time I asked him to go out with Jarvis and me he turned his nose up at the very thought of an all gay establishment, telling me that he would rather stay at home than party with a bunch of sissy-acting fags.

"I thought you didn't do the club thing?" I said an evil stare.

"Yeah, well, I don't normally, but tonight I needed a drink. I'm out with one of my boys. He's drivin' so I had to go where he was goin'. This is where we ended up," Dorey said, still smiling.

"Oh,"

We stood there watching each other for a few moments, me, with a look of detest propelled at Dorey. And Dorey just stood there smiling brightly, showing the same beautiful white teeth that struck me the day we met.

Even though some time had passed, I wasn't at the point where I had moved on. The hurt was still just short of fresh. I had just started to forgive him, and even so, I still hadn't let go of the pain.

Dorey stood there, unfazed by my coldness. I guess he was putting up a front because his friend was standing right next to him and he didn't want to appear to be affected.

His friend looked me up and down with an evil eye similar to the one I had been giving Dorey. By the looks of things, he appeared to be more than just a friend. He was acting a little too protective to be just one of Dorey's "boys." Besides, he looked like he could be Dorey's type. He was my height, my weight and my complexion, just not me.

"Let me find out Dorey is running around with a Jayson look-alike as my replacement," I thought, as I eyed the man standing with Dorey.

With a closer look, I noticed he was nowhere near as attractive, so I didn't feel threatened. And even though Dorey was not mine anymore and I was on the verge of hating him, it was natural for me to feel a little jealous, especially if he had moved on that soon.

"I'm Jayson," I said, holding out my hand to greet Dorey's over-observant friend.

"Oh, *you're* Jayson? I've heard a lot about you. Patrick," he said in response, removing the sketchy look from his face and replacing it with a smile.

"Dance with me," Dorey said as he took his forearm, wrapped it around my waist, pulled me close to him and led me to the dance floor. I didn't want to dance with him, but for some reason I wasn't able to put up a fight.

"So who is your little *friend*?" I asked.

"Oh, that's just one of my boys. It's not like that, I promise."

"I wasn't asking because I'm jealous or anything. I just thought he may be upset with you dancing with me," I lied.

"No, he will be all right,"

We made our way through the crowd, breaking past tightly packed bodies in the packed club so that we could find a place to dance.

Once we found a spot large enough for the both of us, Dorey wasted no time. He grabbed me, pulling me in tight and we danced to the music as he stared deeply into my eyes, never letting go of that damned smile. I felt awkward, as if I was somehow dancing with the devil and even though I knew how bad Satan was, there was no one else I wanted to two-step with.

Initially, I was upset at the sight of my ex, but as we danced my mood softened. While close in his arms, I remembered that familiar feeling I got whenever we were together. It all came back to me. I wanted to stay mad at him, but I couldn't. I wanted to cuss him out and fight him again for all the hurt he had brought, for hiding the truth, for making me love him and for him breaking my heart, but I just didn't have the strength to. As he held me tight and my fever gradually started to break, I realized that love was a dangerous thing, unexplainable and full of power. I was still in love with him.

"So how are things with your health? Are you still staying on top of things?"

"Yeah I'm still okay. I had another small issue about a week ago but I'm fine now, as you can see."

"Dorey, you gotta make sure you take care of yourself."

"Awwww, I knew you still cared," He said smiling as if that were some great surprise.

"I missed you so much, I can't even explain," Dorey said.

I didn't say anything in response, even though I wanted to say that I missed him too and how lonely I had been without him.

"What! You didn't miss me?" he asked, shocked at my silence.

"No," I said adamantly.

He got quiet and seemed dejected, but we didn't stop dancing. Then after a few minutes of just the music playing and the sounds of the club around us, he said to me, "That's okay. I know you're lying."

We got quiet again, dancing song after song until I heard the DJ say "last call" and I knew the club was about to close. It had been more than an hour of nonstop dancing, but to me it only felt like a minute. The entire world had disappeared around us, and I was in a place where only Dorey and I existed. It was a good place, free from hurt, pain and troubled memories. I would have stayed there all night if I could, but it was only an imaginary world and reality was pulling me back.

"Well, I have to go. I know Jarvis is probably waiting for me."

"Hey!" he said, as I began to walk away. He grabbed me by the hand, pulling me back. "I love you."

And for the first time, I didn't say it back. I just walked away, holding my feelings bottled up inside as I scanned the club, looking for Jarvis.

"So was the trip down lover's lane good?" Jarvis asked as we both got into the car.

"What?"

"Don't play stupid. I saw you and Dorey all over each other. You didn't think I saw you, but I did. The whole club did! Anyway, by the way y'all were acting, I would think you two were a couple again."

"No, it's not like that."

"Then what is it like? 'Cause looks sure were deceiving."

"The highway is that way."

"I know how to get to the highway. We're making a quick pit stop before we go home."

"Okay. Where are we going?"

"You just sit back and enjoy the ride. Now, back to you and Dorey. What was that all about?"

"I don't know. Let's not talk about it, though."

"I'm just saying, don't let him get you all caught out there again. Love can be more hazardous to your health than drugs if you let it. Hell, love *is* a drug."

"I said can we *please* not talk about it?"

"Okay."

As we drove around downtown Atlanta, the scenery had grown from familiar to foreign in just a matter of minutes. We had come to a place that looked like it should have been called "the part Atlanta forgot." It looked run down and unsafe. Surprisingly, we weren't the only people around.

"Where are you taking me?"

"We are here."

"And where is here?"

"Just be quiet and pay attention."

There were a few men spread out on the streets. Some walking up and down aimlessly, some were standing fixed in one spot and others were seated on curbs in the background as if they were trying to go unnoticed. This didn't seem like the type of place people would want to just stand around passing time, so what were they doing here, I wondered.

The car slowed down until we were cruising at about five miles an hour as the men looked into the car from their posts. The stares of the men as they examined the inside of our car made me feel unsafe, so I locked the doors while still trying to determine what was going on.

"Jarvis, what are you doing?"

"Shhhhhhh!"

Jarvis then stopped the car, turned of the lights and motioned for one of the guys to come over.

"What the fuck are you doing?"

"About to have some fun. Just relax."

The guy walked over slowly, silently and with an askew gait. He came to the driver's side of the car with his hands in his pockets as Jarvis rolled down his window. He was short and stocky, wearing light blue jeans and a white hooded sweatshirt pulled down over his face so that only a portion of it was revealed to the night. I could barely see his eyes, but what I could see and judging by his mannerisms, he appeared to be under the influence of something. He seemed to be on his own far-out planet and barely aware that we were there, too busy scanning his surroundings like someone was secretly chasing him.

"What are you getting into?" the man asked, as he looked around the street suspiciously and then leaned slowly into the car.

"You!" Jarvis said quietly, which shocked me. I always knew Jarvis was bold, but I had never seen him in such rare form. He hadn't even been drinking that night.

"How much?" Jarvis asked.

"What are you trying to do?" the man asked.

"What do you do?"

"Ten for head, twenty to fuck, twenty-five for both" the man responded bluntly.

"Cool. Well, I want to see what I'm getting first before we do this."

Oh my God, this man is a hoe. I thought to myself as he and Jarvis continued their troubling conversation.

My mind was spinning by then. I couldn't believe what was going on. This guy was a prostitute and Jarvis was actually about to pay him for his services. I had never, ever seen this side of my best friend, and it was troubling to say the least. I thought about all the risks that were involved in what he was doing and how he had said this would be fun. This was miles away from a good time and a lot closer to "Let Me Get The Hell Out Of Here Boulevard."

We had just left the club, a place where Jarvis could have had his pick of any man that would have been more than happy to sleep with him for free. Not saying that a one-night-stand would have been any better than picking up a prostitute, but it would have probably been safer and it wasn't a crime.

The man pulled up his sweatshirt, began to unzip his pants then fulfilled Jarvis' request. I pretended not to see him standing there holding himself as Jarvis gawked in amazement. In my astonishment I kept wondering, "What has Jarvis gotten me into?"

Just then Jarvis put his foot on the gas and the car quickly accelerated. He broke out into frenzied laughter as I turned around and watched the man he had just left on the street. He was holding up both of his middle fingers high in the air and cursing us with his pants still unzipped, his dick fully exposed for a moment until he tucked himself back into his baggy blue jeans.

"What was that?"

Jarvis continued to laugh so hard that tears fell from his eyes. I failed to see the humor in what was going on. I just looked at Jarvis, puzzled as he continued to laugh and we circled the block coming back to the same block we had just left.

Once Jarvis stopped laughing, he let me know what he was up to. He said he would come down this street sometimes after the club just to pass time before going back home, especially if the club was boring. He would come here to make up for what the club lacked. Explaining that he didn't have the intentions to pick anyone up or take them home, professing to be much too classy for that. He said he would just get the men to strip for a laugh. I had to ask why he found so much humor in messing with the men on the street and if he felt bad for playing with their emotions while they were out trying to make a living.

"How would you feel if they came to your job and messed with you?"

"Jayson, you know when I'm not singing I work in customer service. People mess with me all day long. That's part of my job. So now what Mother Teresa? Besides, most of them are too high to even realize what century this is."

That night we circled the block four times, doing the same thing we had done to the first man. I must admit, around the third time I had relaxed a bit and found a little humor in what was going on. By the fourth time I actually got a good look at the man's privates when he whipped it out, instead of playing bashful as I had with the other three.

"You know you are crazy, right?" I asked Jarvis as we drove home, in uncontrollable hysteria.

"Yep! I know," he said.

13

The heavens smiled on me and the storm finally began to pass. There, just over the horizon, was sunshine. The dawning of a new day emerged.

To my surprise, I discovered the book of poetry I wrote was not just a memory. In my drunken depression, when I set it ablaze and erased the file from my computer, thankfully I was too drunk to recall sending two copies of the finished book to the Library of Congress in Washington, D.C., to secure a copyright. That standard procedure of protecting my work had literally changed my life. About seven weeks after putting my manuscript in the mail, it came back with the completed copyright. As I tore open the package seeing the work that I'd thought was gone forever, I realized the receipt of that parcel was my sign never to stop my passion of writing.

Soon after, I began researching various publishing companies. I debated going the traditional route or if I should self publish in order to save myself possible rejection and hurt feelings stemming from rejection. While making my decision fear came, making me question if my work was even good enough to be released to the public. Could my pride withstand people not embracing something that I worked so hard on and put so much of my heart into?

After all my deliberation I decided to see if any publishing houses would be interested in taking a chance on me first, and use self publishing as plan 'B' if necessary.

Then the waiting game began.

Just before I was able to get discouraged from the lack of positive feedback on a publishing deal came great news. A local literary agent by the name of Stacy Pinkney called. Although unsure of how she got my telephone number or how she found out about my work, it didn't matter because the information she shared made me forget about anything else.

Stacy let me know that Barton Press, a somewhat small publishing house based out of New York was very interested in my work. She told me that if I agreed to let her represent me, she could guarantee at least a two-book, five-figure deal with a publishing house like Barton. I was ecstatic. Though I'd never heard of Barton and it wasn't one of the big name publishers whose names were synonymous with success, honestly that type of offer was much more than I expected.

All my fears, anxiety, and insecurities about if my work was ready for the world evaporated as I signed my first publishing deal with Barton Publishing. It seemed that no sooner than I was through writing my signature on the contract, did time quickly begin to increase its pace. After getting the deal with Barton my life became a whirlwind of meetings and deadlines in order to get my work ready for its release. So far I'd already met with publicists, editors, marketing executives and a handful of other people, each had their own role in making my work as profitable as possible. At times things seemed overwhelming, but I would be a terrible liar without admitting enjoying every moment.

After a whirlwind weekend in New York, my soul couldn't have been happier to be on the way back to Atlanta. Though the past few days were wonderful and filled with per diems, and all expenses paid, it came at a price. Constant meetings, hidden chaos, and the inability to enjoy my free stay had me longing for the comforts of home.

As the red fasten seatbelt lights that had been illuminating the planes darkened interior lost their glow, I stood up in unison with dozens of the other passengers onboard the redeye flight 337. We'd just landed in Atlanta's Hartsfield Airport from New York and everyone around me was looking as tired as my body felt. I grabbed my carry on bag, then followed behind a line full of the tired looking travelers as we exited.

Somewhere between leaving the plane and my first few steps off into the airport, my bladder became to full to focus on anything else but its release. As my eyes spotted the nearest restroom, within moments me and my bag where inside it and posted at the nearest stall.

"What's good folk?"

I had been too focused on myself to notice that I was no longer alone. It was amusing that no matter how many open urinals there could be in a public restroom someone always managed to find the one right next to me and strike up a conversation.

"Oh, im chillin." I said in a way that should have let him know that I wasn't in the mood for talking.

"So where are you going?"

"Home. I just got back from New York and I'm tired as hell."

"Oh ok cool, I've been there a few times its…"

Jayson you can be downright rude sometimes you know that? I said to myself as I cut the unwanted conversation short and quickly left the bathroom, eager to get to my car and go home.

"Shit!" I exclaimed as I finally made it to my car after sprinting through the airport with my heavy bag only to find that my keys had been left in the cars ignition all weekend.

Thankfully no one had stolen my car, but what was I going to do without my keys?

After all the foul words in my vocabulary had been depleted, I sat on the hood of my car trying to brainstorm on how to get inside. Was it worth breaking my window and paying to have it fixed? Should I call a locksmith and wait for hours until they came and then pay to have them get me into my own car? Or would it be best to take a taxi or public transportation home and figure out a better remedy later when I wasn't so tired?

"You again." I heard a voice saying from behind.

"You must be following me."

"Nah folk I heard somebody out here cussin' and actin' a damn fool, so I looked to see what was going on and when I did…"

"Dude, just say you were following me" I said breaking a much needed smile.

"Ok, if that makes you feel better about your situation, then yeah I was following you."

"I locked my keys in the car."

"Is that all? The way you were carrying on, it seemed serious."

"It is serious, I'm tryna get home."

"Well what about this, I get you in your car and I wont charge you anything but a ride."

"Ok. Cool but how are you going to get into my car?"

"Just stand back, pay attention and you might learn something."

"Do your thing."

"First, I know you have a wire hanger in that bag."

"I do" I said as I opened my bag, pulled out a hanger and took the shirt off of it.

Within minutes, the door was unlocked and the man was standing there speechless with an arrogant smirk.

What was I doing? In this moment of clouded judgment I had let go of all that was rational, all that was logical and before I could think, it had already happened. Ecstatic over the fact that I know had my keys and the ability to finally go home, giving the man a simple ride to where he needed to go seemed to be the least I could do.

I stared at him, wondering why I had let this complete stranger get inside my car. Only a complete idiot would do what I was doing. This guy could have been a serial killer, murderer, rapist or even a psycho for all I knew. He seemed nice enough, but only knowing him for less than a few minutes there was no way of knowing what he was capable of.

Visions of my name and face on the 10 o'clock news danced through my head as I sat in the car staring at the stranger. I imagined a reporter covering the late-breaking details of my gruesome murder, explaining how they found me dead in a dumpster or in some back alley, my torso full of bullets.

The stranger held out his right hand and introduced himself.

"Wassup, folk?" he said. "Red."

"Huh?" I asked.

"Red, folk. They call me Red."

"Oh. I'm Jayson,"

I caught myself staring and quickly tried to divert my attention to the empty road ahead.

"Thanks for letting me ride."

"Yeah, no problem," I said.

Judging from the smell that had filled the interior of my car, Red had been drinking, either that or he was wearing some kind of rum-scented cologne, which I seriously doubted. By the tone in his voice he had consumed enough liquor to really feel the spirits' effects. His words were slightly slurred and he had this distant, glassy, look in his eyes.

It had gone somewhat unnoticed until that moment but, while steeling glances I couldn't help but notice Red's attractiveness. He was tall, about 6'2", had a slim build and was bathed in a unique, reddish-brown complexion. I figured his smooth, red skin had something to do with how he got his nickname. He had large, gentle and distinctive brown eyes which first caught my attention, while his personality held it.

"Red, where are you going?"

He sat there in silence for a minute, and then said, "I'll show you. Make a left at this light."

My worries came back like a flood.

Troubling thoughts started to race through my head almost as fast as my heartbeat. What if this man was taking me somewhere secluded so he could pull out a gun, shoot me, steal my car and wallet, leaving me for dead? But foolishly, the naivety in me decided to give Red the benefit of the doubt because he seemed far too kind to be a murderer.

Soon, we'd arrived at a street with only two parked cars. The street was very still and I didn't see anyone. Red instructed me to pull over up the street and park. Without any hesitation, I did as he said.

"What's over here?" I asked.

"This is the spot."

"The spot?"

"Yeah, folk, you know, the spot."

I gave Red a puzzled look; I had no idea what he was talking about. I didn't know where I was, and didn't know what "the spot" meant in reference to this place.

"So do you live around here?" I asked, thinking maybe he meant his spot, as in his house. But there were no houses in sight.

"Nah, I don't live around here," Red said slyly.

The inability to figure things out left me with an urgency to know what was going on. I had never rode in the same car with a stranger, but I figured when someone wanted a ride, they were trying to get to an actual destination. This place Red led me to was definitely nothing but a desolate street.

"So what's up?" I quizzed.

Red then grabbed my hand, took it off the steering wheel and placed it in his lap.

"You feel that?" he asked. "That's what's up!"

I didn't know what to do. I just looked at him for a minute, trying to fight the strong smell of alcohol coming from him when he spoke until I could no longer take the awkward feeling mounting in me. Then I looked away, trying my best not to appear thrown by what was taking place, almost forgetting about the fact that my hand was still on his crotch.

Red began to unzip his pants while he took my hand and hid it inside his gray, cotton boxer-briefs. My hands then became full and as I felt myself growing even more worried with each passing second. I quickly removed my hand from Red's and placed it back on the steering wheel, still gazing into the distance. I fought to act cool and calm like I was oblivious to the panic that had beset me.

He grabbed my face, unfazed by my disinterest and placed his full lips on mine, exploring my body with his hands. I wondered if this was his attempt at a sexual assault, or if he was just trying to get some because he thought I was showing signs of interest.

For some uncertain reason I stopped trying to fight the moment. Maybe it was because I hadn't been kissed like that for far too long or maybe it was because his lips felt so good against mine. Unsure of why, I began to let go while tasting the warmth and liquor in his mouth.

His forceful way felt good as I began to loosen up and relax while under the trance of his masculinity. What were the odds of picking up a first-time stranger and it being like this?

Suddenly, I grew confident, and the previous thoughts of possible danger were tossed aside.

We kissed for a while before he suddenly pulled away. My eyes fell into his lap where his thick, exposed flesh was waiting on his thigh. He had pulled his pants and underwear all the way down, revealing everything. Red couldn't help but follow my eyes down to his naked skin as he said, "So what are you going to do with that?"

I looked at him sharply, stunned by his ever-increasing forwardness and said, "Nothing!"

By that point I had become very horny, so much so that my own skin was uncomfortably filling my underwear as my mannish nature was almost to a level of taking over the remains of the better judgment I hadn't already thrown away.

I thought about what I would like to do with Red, but I couldn't even believe I had let myself kiss him so passionately after just meeting him, and without even knowing his real name.

Though the offer was very tempting, I just couldn't accept.

"You don't want none of this?' he asked as he started to take his hard flesh in his hands and seductively stroke himself.

"Nah, I don't even know you," I said.

"You really don't remember me?" he asked, taking a pause from pleasure.

"Should I?" I quizzed, looking him over thoroughly, wondering if I had met him before. Usually I never forgot faces and from his certainness, he made it seem as if he knew me.

Red sat silently while I watched him closely trying to figure out why and how I might know him. Then it hit me. How could I have forgotten a set of brown eyes like his? I had seen him before. Though we weren't formally introduced we had met, very briefly. He was the fourth man on the strip my first night back in Atlanta, the one I had actually gotten a good look at. He looked so different tonight, but his eyes were the same. Red was one of the men we had pretended to be interested in paying in order to get a free flash, before driving off in a fit of laughter without even giving him the chance to compose himself.

"Ohhhh, I do remember..."

"Yeah, you remember me now."

"Yes."

Suddenly the fact that I'd kissed him so passionately brought imaginations of all the places his mouth had been and what he may have done with it, and I wanted to vomit.

"I remembered you, too. How could I forget someone so cute? I really wish you would have stayed that night," he said.

"Look, me and..."

I tried to explain to him what me and Jarvis were doing the night of our initial meeting and apologize, fearing that we had pissed him off and he would take his anger out on me now that we were alone. He cut me off before I could finish.

"It's cool. Don't even trip about it. I already know the deal," he said.

"Okay," I replied.

After that we sat in the car, totally silent for a few minutes. We made a few horribly failed attempts at small talk, but it didn't take long for Red to resume a shot at his previous agenda.

"So, let me ask you this. What did you think was going to happen when I got in your car?" he asked.

"I thought you were someone who needed a ride and that I would help you out. You helped me get in my car and I was grateful. That's all!"

"Yeah? Well you can help me out, and yeah I do want to ride. I want to ride that ass," he said as he struggled to climb into the backseat of my car, and then took my arm and pulled me back there with him.

"Red, you are cute and all, but I don't have casual sex."

"Oh, really?" he said as he gently coerced my head in his lap. I could still tell, not to mention, feel, that he was trying his hardest to get sex.

I laid there in his lap, still and quiet for what seemed like an eternity as Red gently rubbed my hair and occasionally played with my ears or leaned down to plant a kiss.

I can't even lie. It felt really good being in the company of this sexy stranger, even if he was a hustler. It had been too long since I had been able to enjoy the company of another man and I had almost forgotten how good it felt just to be held.

My repulsion for Red and his chosen profession subsided with each soft stroke of his hand. While he gently rubbed my head I resumed enjoying his touch.

Red finally broke the silence when he asked one last time what I wanted to do. I stood firm on my previous response, explaining again that I had never done anything like this before and even though I found him very attractive, I just wasn't the type of person who felt comfortable doing anything more than we had already done.

To back up my stance against casual sex, I started talking about AIDS and my extreme fear of one day catching it. To my surprise he started sharing with me.

"Yeah, I've known a few people to die of AIDS. It makes you really think sometimes. Even though I do what I do, I'm not one of those dirty niggas that don't use condoms, and I get tested."

"Why?" I asked.

"Why what? *Why do I get tested*?" Red asked with surprise.

"There are a lot of other ways to get money. Why like this? You are way too cute and seem to intelligent to be using you body for a few dollars," I said.

Red got quiet and after about a minute, all he could say was, "I know, but I didn't used to be like this."

Not sure of what else to say, the two of us just sat there trapped in another moment of awkward silence.

"I gotta go now," Red said with a shift in mood.

"Where you on your way to? I'll drop you off."

"Back to the airport."

It was so quiet in the car. I honestly couldn't think of anything to say, and I was still shocked by all that had transpired.

A spark of compassion ignited as I wondered about how it could have been me in Red's shoes if things in my life hadn't worked out for the better. If Jarvis hadn't let me stay with him and things with my book weren't going good, would I have resorted to pimping myself to make ends meet?

Before saying goodbye, I felt the need to give him some money. My heart really went out to him and he seemed like he could really use some extra cash, so I reached into my pants pocket to get out my wallet, only it wasn't there.

I knew I had my wallet earlier that evening because I needed my ID to board the plane. Trying to backtrack my steps, I quickly gave up figuring it had to be either in my bag or somewhere in the car.

"I'm sorry if I disappointed you in any way," I said.

"It's cool, folk. But there is one thing you can do for me before you go."

"What's that?"

"Write your number down. It was cool talking to you, but we didn't get to finish."

I smiled while searching around my car for a piece of paper and something to write with. Again came a moment when I couldn't explain my actions. Why was I giving him my number? Then I realized how refreshing it was meeting him in spite of everything and figured what the hell? Besides, the first thing I was going to do once I found my wallet was find Red and give him the money that I wanted to give him at that moment. I wrote my number down, handed it to him and we quickly exchanged smiles as I drove off. I headed home smiling as I recapped the evenings interesting events.

"Muthafukka you are one crazy, sick, sonofabitch!" Jarvis said.

I called to tell him about my day and about Red, unable to wait until I made it home to share the news with him. Jarvis, being the no-holds-barred type, quickly let me have it, telling me that I was crazy to let a stranger get in my car. That fact I already knew.

"Boy, it is the new millennium! People get shot up and chopped up when they do stupid shit like that. Now I know you are naïve and all, but that was just plain dumb. I feel bad for introducing you to the stroll now. Yeah, I go out there, but I never let anyone in my car. I can't believe you," he fussed.

"I know, I know, but I didn't know who he was when he first got in the car and I met him at the airport, not the stroll." I said matter-of-factly, not at all expecting that kind of response from my wild and crazy best friend.

"Didn't your mamma ever tell you not to talk to strangers?

"And now that I'm done cussing you out, on to bigger and better things. What did his piece look like?" Jarvis quizzed, changing the subject.

I just had to laugh. That was one thing about Jarvis. He was completely tactless and said whatever was on his mind, no matter how off the wall it was. If he was feeling it, he was saying it. I pretended that I didn't hear his question, but he quickly repeated it, protesting being ignored.

"I know you heard me! What about the piece, damn it?"

"It was nice."

"Nice? What is that supposed to mean? *Nice* is how you describe a two-week vacation getaway in the south of France, not a ding-a-ling. I need details!"

"I'm almost home I'll give you details later." I said, trying to change the subject.

"Where are you now?"

"Riding down I-85, I took the long way cause I don't have money for the toll on 400."

"Jayson, please don't tell me you lost your wallet again. What is this, like, the hundredth time?"

"No it's around here somewhere. I'm just a little disorganized right now."

"Okay. And I like the way you *tried* to change the subject. As I remember we were talking about this *Red's* penis," he said.

I couldn't contain my laughter. Jarvis was a fool, but that's probably why we were such good friends. He kept everything really light and never let much get him down.

Just then, my call waiting alerted me that another call was coming through. Saved by the bell I thought, not wanting to go into any further details.

"Jarvis, that's my mother on the other line. I'll call you back," I said.

"Not before you answer my question, you're not," he demanded.

"It was like an Anaconda. I'll tell you more when I get home," I said, just imagining the look on his face as I clicked over to the call waiting on my other line.

14

Take a few cups of loneliness, about a quart of curiosity, three tablespoons of wonderment of backtracking to a life with Dorey, a teaspoon of horniness, and a dash of spite, combine them all and let them ferment just long enough that the ingredients become stronger than pure grain alcohol, and there you would have the makings of me.

Things started out with an occasional phone call, and then quickly progressed to daily talks where I found myself intrigued with the man on the other end of the line. There was a severe contrast between my mental image of what someone like Red should be and what he actually was. I found myself flirting with disaster and growing increasingly curious. Strangely, I felt something developing but just couldn't stop the forces of human nature like I'd planned.

I was no Richard Gere, he was no Julia Roberts, and my life was far from the plot of *Pretty Woman*. So why couldn't I snap out of this growing curiosity for Red?

Common sense should have kept me far from the thought of entertaining a man at that current place in my life. But, common sense wasn't strong enough to make me put aside the natural desire to feel important and loved.

There I was juggling between the idea of a date with Red and finally reconciling with Dorey. That overwhelming decision was starting to take time away from my book, so something had to give.

Damn that boy, his cute, big brown eyes, and the fact that he was just so sexy and so damned persistent! I thought to myself. I didn't quite understand how it was that in just a few short hours I would be going out on a date with someone like Red. He had been relentless in his pursuit of me and after a while, finally achieving what I thought impossible, getting me to agree to go out with him. He broke me down and after lots of debate, I finally said "yes."

There were so many things I had to think about before agreeing to go out with Red. First and foremost was the fact that he was a male whore. Clear-cut and dry, that's just what he was. Though he said he didn't do it often and was going to quit real soon, he still was a whore. Not a whore in the sense that he slept around with random people, but an actual whore who was getting paid for sex.

Red preferred the term "sexual therapist" or a "hustler" and couldn't stand being called a "whore." "trick" or any of the other not-so-politically correct names that referred to his chosen profession. The fact remained that any fancy title you put on what he did still couldn't alter the fact that he sold his body for money, which made me very uncomfortable.

How would I look dating a prostitute? Then, I started thinking about how cute he was, how much I liked his personality and remembered the good vibes I got from him after the phone conversations we had, not to mention the almost electric feeling I felt when we kissed.

Red's personality seemed so genuine and down to earth. He wasn't stuck on himself or uptight and possessed the sincerity I looked for but so rarely found. Finally, I forced myself to take a chance, forget about what other people might think, not make plans for a future with him just yet, and just enjoy a date, something I hadn't had for far too long. I agreed to one date, shutting out any possible deep romantic feelings and any thoughts of letting things go any further.

Jarvis knew all about the situation. He thought I had gone completely crazy for entertaining Red's company. But after he saw how sweet Red was during a brief phone interrogation, he actually encouraged me to take a chance with Red.

"Jayson," he said. "The fact is you *need* a date. This guy is offering, so go. Just make sure you take my mace with you and call me if he even looks at you funny 'cause you know I'll be there."

Within a few days of making my final decision, I gave Red a call and nervously hinted that we could go out, telling him I would be available on Saturday if he was still interested. He said of course and a few minutes later we had made plans for dinner and a movie.

At 8:30 the bastard was a half hour late. He hadn't even had the decency to so much as call to let me know anything. You would think that after practically begging for a chance to show his potential and that he was genuinely interested, that the least he could do was be on time.

At nine o'clock I still hadn't heard anything from Red, I assumed I had been stood up and I was just short of furious. As I began to undress and prepare for another Saturday evening at home, I thought for a moment while sitting on the couch in the living room watching an episode of "I Love Lucy" that I'd seen at least 20 times, that it almost served me right getting stood up. I had been acting so high and mighty and so disinterested in the whole date. While I was up on my soapbox, I had failed to realize that I was human and had my fair share of drama.

Suddenly, I felt the urge to get out of the house. If I wasn't going on a date, there was no need for me to sit around the house and sulk. I threw on an old t-shirt, jacket and jeans then headed out of the apartment. I was just going to go drive around the city for a while to calm my nerves. Driving around town in my car may not have been as nice as dinner and a movie, but I didn't really have many other options.

Walking toward the car, I could hear a faint noise that sounded like someone calling my name. In order to be sure I wasn't hearing things, I paused. There it was again, my name being called in the night. It was too low and far off to recognize, but when I looked around, I saw a figure off in the distance motioning for my attention. As it jogged closer, I saw it was Red. He stopped to catch his breath and barked out, "Sorry I'm late."

I wanted to lash out at him, but rethought things briefly as I stood watching him. I was slightly taken back by the way he looked. My eyes slowly made their way up his body, starting at his feet until I was staring into his hypnotic eyes.

Everything he had on looked new and he appeared to be so polished and well put together that he could double as a living mannequin from some upscale boutique. He had on dark brown dress shoes, dark gray slacks pressed nicely, a lighter gray dress shirt and a tie that blended everything together perfectly. I was thoroughly impressed.

His cologne filled me, making me patient. He had gone through a great deal of effort to look nice, and there I was in my t-shirt and jeans.

Red looked so incredible I almost overlooked the bottle of wine and beautiful bouquet of flowers he was holding.

"You clean up real well," I admitted.

Somehow my anger dissipated. All was now forgiven and I was anxious to get our date started.

"Thank you," he replied as his lips broke into a smile.

"Are those for me?" I asked, coyly referring to the gifts he held.

"Oh, yeah. I almost forgot. These are for you."

"Thank you!"

"And they say that romance is dead," he said sarcastically.

Red took a moment to explain that he had been trying to locate me, but accidentally left the slip of paper he had jotted my number and address on at home.

"I was just going to hang around at your car. Sooner or later you would have to come out of your apartment," he said.

"Why didn't you just go back home and get the address and number? You could have been there and back by now."

"No, I wouldn't have. I caught the bus over here, and by the time I would have gotten home and caught another bus back over here, it would be tomorrow. Look, I'm so sorry, but let me start by making it up to you now."

It sure is going to be hard not to like this man, I thought as Red held out his hand, waiting for me to give him mine. I shook his hand as he quickly grabbed it and he pulled me in close, seductively giving me a soft peck on the back of my hand.

"So where were you about to go?"

"I thought you had stood me up and I was on my way downtown to find something to do."

"I would never stand you up," he said as he kissed my neck and the words echoed sweetly off my skin, making me feel warmth inside.

"Stop, Red!" I exclaimed, "What are you trying to do, get us gay bashed out here?" I asked playfully.

"Boy, please. I would like to see the person who would even try to mess with me tonight. I feel like I'm on top of the world. I have a beautiful man with me who finally came to his senses and let me spend some time with him. Nobody can mess up this night.

I found myself smiling. Being in his presence had me feeling all child-like and giddy, like back in the days of grade school romance, back when things were so much simpler, before life was complicated. Back when you would hit someone to let them know how much you liked them or asked someone out in a note rather than in person. That night was a throwback to the good old days I'd experienced as a child, days filled with innocence, laughter and free from reservation. We did a whole lot of smiling and I ended up not wanting the night to end.

The best part was that Red remained a total gentleman from the start of the date until the he walked me back to the apartment and I shut the door. He never once tried anything, not even a kiss. We ended up hugging goodbye, but there were no sexual advances, just innocent enjoyment of each other.

When I got home from my date I found Jarvis was camped out in the living room like a security guard on patrol. Although he appeared to be in a deep sleep, passed out on the sofa, as I quietly crept past him to get to my bedroom, he sprung up like a jack-in-the-box and started asking all the questions he had obviously been waiting up to ask.

"Although I don't want to admit it, I like him, Jarvis. I really like him," I said, still reeling.

"How was it?"

"*Good.*"

"Um hmm. Judging from the way you said '*good,*' it sounds like y'all had a really *good* time. And by the smile on your face, I would almost venture to guess that the drought is over and you finally got laid. I just hope y'all used condoms," Jarvis said.

"Nope, it didn't go that far; we just had a really good time," I said.

"Oh, I forgot you lost your wallet so the two of you couldn't have had sex since you couldn't pay."

"That was low," I said.

That comment suddenly stopped my smile in its tracks. The unwanted reminder of Red's situation, the one thing I had let myself block from my mind, came back, slapping me right in the face. I had such a good time with him that I didn't once think about anything negative. Then again, I guess the high had to wear off sooner or later.

"I'm only playing. What did y'all do?" he asked.

"Dinner and a movie. We ended up talking in the car after dinner so long that we fell asleep. It felt so perfect," I said, neglecting to tell Jarvis how Red had shown up late only because that would have detracted from my story.

"Damn, let me fasten my seatbelt 'cause this story is just *soooo* interesting. Y'all two crazy kids really shouldn't do such wild and off the wall things on a first date. I mean, really, leave some excitement for date number two," Jarvis said, his voice dripping with sarcasm.

"Shut up!" I replied. "Sorry I can't be more like you and have my dates handcuffed naked to the bed on the first date. And besides, I wasn't trying to see him on that level, remember?"

"So, the two of you had *big fun* talking all night long, huh? And what did you find out about him?"

"I found out a lot. And I already knew a lot" I said.

"Oh really, what's his last name?"

"Don't know."

"What kind of car does he drive?"

"He rides the bus," I replied as I saw the look on Jarvis' face go from normal to the sour response of someone who had just took a big bite from a lemon.

"Has he ever been married? Have any kids? Is he gay, bi, or…"

"I don't know,"

"Well, hell, what did y'all talk about? It couldn't have been each other 'cause it sounds like you don't know anything about this guy other than he's a cute hoe."

"You're absolutely right, Jarvis. We didn't talk about each other, but I like that we didn't. I like that the date wasn't saturated with feelings of awkwardness or barraged with a million and one questions like, 'So what do you do? What's your favorite movie? What do you like to do in your spare time? When was your last relationship and how long did it last? What's your….'"

"All right, all right! I got your point," Jarvis interrupted.

"Besides, when people ask you those questions on the first date, it's more habitual than genuine interest. It's like they feel as though asking those questions makes them seem interested. Most men forget the answers you gave on date one by date number two. That is *if* there is a date two," I continued.

"You know, that's true…" Jarvis admitted.

"Yep, but it wasn't that. We did more talking than asking questions, and the conversation flowed. We talked about real life, issues that matter more than just what kind of car he drives or what we like to do sexually," I said, showing slight signs of agitation.

The truth is Jarvis was effectively taking away the wonderful feeling that I had captured, that first-date high that you seldom experience. I wanted to savor the euphoria for as long as I could. Instead, Jarvis replaced it with the sting of premature reality. I wasn't ready to come back to that harsh realism yet.

"Well, excuse me and my narrow-minded ass. I am so sorry that my dates are so *typical* and the conversations are *general*, usually ending in a one-night-stand, but that's all I need right now. You know, Jayson, not everybody is looking for love or their prince charming to come whisk them away and live happily ever after. Some of us don't want Mr. Right, but instead just a Mr. Right Now to fulfill our natural human desires, and then leave with no strings attached."

"Jarvis, it's okay that you're a slut, I love you anyway. But you may want to think about charging like Red does. That way you will have a purpose." I said jokingly, trying to avoid an argument and maybe keep one speck of post-date bliss.

"To hell with you," he said laughing.

I sat beaming for a second until reality reared its ugly head again.

"So when is the next date?" he asked.

Before the date, I had tried so hard not to like Red and promised myself that there would be only one date. I never imagined that he would capture and hold my attention. Red and I hadn't discussed it, but to me a second date seemed like the only possible next step, even though I wasn't sure I was ready for date number two--at least not yet. He was cool, had a great personality, could hold a conversation, was smart and good looking, but what about the not so good things?

Just then the phone rang, cutting our conversation short. I noticed that it was the number Red always called from and didn't hesitate to answer it by the end of the first ring.

"Hello?"

"What's going on, beautiful?" It was Red and suddenly an even wider smile filled my already glowing face.

"I really enjoyed you last night," he said.

"I really enjoyed you, too, Red."

"I want to see you again."

That was quick, I thought. He was already asking for a second date within hours of our first. Although I really had a good time and wanted to see him again as well, I had not yet sorted through my feelings. I wasn't sure I was ready for something to happen with him and I knew the more dates we had, the greater the chance something would happen. Be it lust, love or anything in between.

Silence filled the line while I thought and Red waited for my answer.

"So you're just going to leave me out there like that? You blow my mind with an incredible first date, get me feeling you and then act like I can't come back for more?" Red asked.

"I'll go out with you again," I said. The words came out of my mouth before my brain had time to process them.

Damn what did I just do? I thought.

"Good. I'll see you at 8."

"Red! You are supposed to ask me if I have plans first. You can't just assume that I'm free," I said.

"Oh, well do you have plans for tonight, Jayson?" he asked with hesitation.

"No, none come to mind."

"Well, good. I will see you at 8," he said.

"Will you remember my number and address this time?"

"I promise I will."

"Oh, and one more thing, Red."

"What's that, baby?"

"What's your real name?"

"Tymes, Brian Tymes. Is this for the background check?" he teased.

As we both said goodbye, the giddy feeling from the previous night returned.

15

"Dorey, we can't do this."

"Do *what*?"

"*This*!" I said, taking his hand and removing it from its place on my thigh. He had been taunting me all morning with his hands and kissing me on the various parts of my body he knew turned me on.

Faking sleep and pretending not to feel Dorey's come-ons was useless. One part of me just would not cooperate with the ruse.

Dorey started haunting my world day and night soon after my first day back in the city. He quickly managed to secure a position placing himself back into my life. Through a "friend of a friend" he discovered that I was staying with Jarvis, then came the frequent calls and unannounced visits accompanied by cards, flowers and gifts.

In a moment of weakness I agreed to see him. Even though Dorey was pushing for much more than just dating and had apologized more than a million times with what seemed to be sincerity, I wasn't ready to take him back with open arms like he wanted. I couldn't deny the inviolable feelings that still ran deep, for he was my first and only love.

Still, those feelings weren't powerful enough to break the chains of bad memories that stood guard around my healing heart. He would have to prove his worth to me before I could let go and allow myself to love and trust him enough to grant him a second invitation inside my world.

His touch felt so warm, soothing and even better than I remembered. Then, after just a second of selfish indulgence, getting caught up in the moment, I could no longer hide the fact that I was physically aroused.

Full of vulnerability, I was caught in a position where I had to decide what to follow, my head or my heart. Though the two organs came from the same body, each had its own agenda and each was saying something that was a direct opposite of what the other craved.

I was caught in a virtual tug of war. My head was telling me to be wise and not get involved with this man, no matter how much I loved him, how much it may hurt to let him go and not think about what I may be missing out on by not giving him a second chance.

My heart wanted to fall in love with Dorey all over again, and it thought the pain endured was worth experienceing, because the good times superseded anything else. It told me that my life hadn't been right without Dorey, and it *needed* him back.

But I decided to play it smart; I tried listening to my head, trying to stop things before they got started, because it was my heart that had gotten me into so much trouble in the first place.

I agreed to let him sleep in my bed night before, after we got in late from yet another dinner date, but I should have resisted. It was evident that by letting him sleep in my bed, fighting temptation was where it would lead. We never had been able to just sleep in a bed when we were alone and lying next to each other, so it was foolish of me to think things would be any different this time.

"What's wrong?" Dorey asked.

"I just don't think that this is a good idea," I said.

"A good idea? What is there to think about? I'm horny, you're *obviously* horny, too, and it's not like we've never done this before," he said as he climbed on top of me, talking low and sexy in my ear with his seductive bedroom voice, still trying his best to convince me to give in.

With his flesh pressed firmly into mine, I could feel that his point of arousal was almost higher than mine. It was becoming increasingly harder to say no.

"I ca-*can't* do this," I said.

"Are you sure?" he asked, straddling my body, and then moving in toward me again until his lips were touching my forehead and I could feel his warm words dancing on my temples.

His actions continued to heighten the desire locked inside of me, kicking it into overdrive, to a peak where I could barely resist.

Then, just as I should have predicted, the short battle of will was quickly brought to end with a few delicate kisses on my forehead and temples.

I grabbed him and started to kiss him while memories of all the times I'd wanted him so badly, but couldn't have him came back to me like a flood. I remembered the times we were apart and I secretly longed to have his body back in my bed, holding me so tightly I couldn't breathe, just so I knew he was there and wasn't going anywhere ever again. I remembered the days that I was overcome with tears and wanted just one kiss from him to make everything okay, even though I hated him for the pain he made me feel. I still loved him for everything he was. So I kissed him long and I kissed him hard with all the passion I had been storing, and then began to undress him.

After all of his clothes were off and he was naked before me, the sexual frustration I tried to undo left me not wanting to waste a single second on foreplay. Forgoing foreplay, I zeroed in on what I had been missing the most.

I wanted him badly as I climbed on top of him, and then grinded my body over his, watching him squirm with pleasure. He grabbed my waist, pulling me in close until our bodies were pressed so tightly together there was no room for anything between us.

I paused for a moment so that I could get a condom and some lubrication from the top drawer of my nightstand. I opened the condom wrapper, and then placed it in my mouth, while maintaining eye contact with Dorey. I revealed to him subliminally how much I needed him. Still gazing deep in his eyes, no words were necessary, my eyes and my body scream-ed out loud everything I felt.

Dorey was lying flat on his back as I took my hand and brushed it lightly against his eyes, signaling him to close them. Then I bent over his waist and slowly started to slide the condom on his sex with my mouth. He roared with pas-sion, and then opened his eyes, looking up to see what I had done to bring him such pleasure.

"Oh, shit!" he said, as his eyes started to roll back in his head.

After the condom was all the way on, I put some lubrication on him then resumed my position on top, eagerly anticipating and preparing myself for what was about to take place.

"You know what? Maybe you were right and this wasn't such a good idea," he said, moving my body from on top of his and pushing me to the side.

I was shocked. He couldn't be serious.

"What!" I said, frustrated, trying to make sure I heard him correctly. I couldn't believe that after all of his advances, all the sweet talk and all the waiting he endured, he was turning me down now that the moment he had been waiting for was there in front of him.

I knew Dorey too well to believe he could resist me, and while I watched his mouth telling me that it wasn't a good idea, I also saw his lower half silently speaking opposition. Its hardness told another story. Then again, maybe he was serious. He had stopped all advances and turned on the television, an entirely different mood overtaking him.

I got up from the bed and walked toward the bath-room, trying to walk off my anger. As horny as I was, this was the last thing I wanted. I simply could not believe what had just occurred. Once I was sure my back was turned and he could no longer see my facial expressions, I started to pout like a child, as I sulked slowly toward the bathroom, trying to keep my cool until totally out of view.

Just then, Dorey came running up behind me, grabbing me tight in his arms. Then he picked me up and threw me back on the bed while I looked at him like he had gone insane. What in the world was he up to with these confusing antics?

"I was just playing. You didn't think I was really going to pass up all that ass did you?" he asked smacking me on the backside.

"Not if you were as smart as I remember," I said, starting to relax as I caught his game.

Dorey started to laugh as he read right through me, knowing he had pissed me off. I punched him in the chest to let him know his acts were not as amusing as he thought.

"You really had me mad," I said, relieved that he was only playing, because I was in serious need of sexual healing.

"I'm sorry," he said as he started to kiss me all over and we began to have some of the best sex ever. The years and many sexual encounters between us had us to a point were we knew each other's bodies like they were our own. We knew everything about each other, what the other liked and didn't like, our fantasies, fetishes and the spots that made us lose complete control.

That morning, we left each other's every desire more than fulfilled.

After we were finished making love, instead of falling asleep, we lay in the afterglow of the moment. We stayed that way, talking for hours, holding each other like people in the movies and when love is new.

"You know you are the only one I've ever really been in love with, man or woman," Dorey said.

That was not what I was expecting to hear. Usually people said sweet things like that to get you into bed and have their way with you, not after they had already done so.

"What about Shawnquetta?" I asked.

"What about her?" he replied. "She means nothing to me. She is just the mother of my children. I was never in love with her. Never really even loved her." After a long pause, he continued. "You know what, baby? I'm really sorry that you had to fall in love with someone like me."

After the morning we'd shared I couldn't believe what I was hearing. From the words he spoke it seemed like Dorey was leading up to some sort of pitiful apology. Now was definitely not the right time for an 'I'm sorry'. I no longer wanted an apology from him and didn't even want an explanation for why he'd cheated.

One of my mothers favorite quotes was "The truth doesn't need explaining," and she was right. The truth had already been revealed and it was there for the world to see. Growing in Shawnquetta's stomach was the evidence of Dorey's transgression.

Though I didn't have all the details of *where*, *when* and *why*, all that concerned me is that I knew *what* happened.

"Can we not talk about this? I was really enjoying myself and I don't want to ruin it with what you're about to do."

"No! We need to discuss this. How long are we goin' to continue to avoid talking about what happened? We can't just go on pretendin' that everythin' is okay."

"Who is pretending that everything is okay other than you? Everything is far from okay. I just choose to deal with things in my own way. After finding out that the one man I gave my heart to cheated on me and has a child on the way as a result of it, just short of losing all sanity, I had to pick up the pieces of my life and worry about me, 'cause you damn sure didn't seem to care!"

"I did, I mean I do care, and I love you. No one has ever showed me love like you and I know I will never find that in anyone else. I mean you stuck by me through my cancer, took care of me when I was sick, cared about me enough to make sure I was taking care of myself even more than my own mother. And I will always love you for that."

"And you show your love by cheating on me?" I snapped.

"Listen J, I'm really sorry that you had to fall in love with me. After we broke up it caused me to take a real long look at myself and now I'm realizin' that I'm a mess," he said in a pitiful tone.

"Please tell me you are not looking for sympathy."

"No, that's not what I'm lookin' for. I'm just speakin' the truth. Jayson, I am a bisexual man. Not one of those that operates on the principals of 'bi now gay later;' I'm a true bisexual, which means I like ass just as much as I like pussy. Bein' in a three-year commitment with you was incredible, but a strain at the same time…"

"A strain? Oh, you've got to explain this."

"I never expected myself to fall in love with another man. You know you were the first man that I've ever been in a relationship with. It was new, excitin', wonderful and the whole nine. But, at the same time, bein' in love with a man started to weigh on my conscious. You've had much longer to come to terms with your sexuality. Your parents know about you and even though they don't accept it, it still allows you to be more open. My parents don't know about this side of me and I never want them to because it would kill them, if not me first. It was all happenin' too fast and I…"

"Dorey, you are talking in circles and I'm not following you. You are losing me."

"Baby, I know. I'm tryin' to explain the best I can, but it's not… Okay, this is the whole truth from the beginnin' of where I messed up. Remember that night that the phone was off the hook in the bedroom and Shawnquetta overheard us havin' sex? Well, after that night I went to go see her and try to think of somethin' to throw her off. I ended up makin' up a lie about us never bein' together like that before and it was a one-time thing because I was just curious. I told her you got me drunk, took advantage of me, I hated it and would never do it again. After I told her that lie I ended up fuckin' her like crazy, to try and make sure that she didn't continue to question my sexuality.

"Lyin' to her about the nature of our relationship was bad enough, but then cheatin' on you was even worse. It was a terrible thing to do and I will always regret hurtin' you. But at that time I felt like there was no other way. She was talkin' about tellin' my friends and family about us and keepin' my daughter from me. I just couldn't risk that. You know how much I love Jasmine," he said.

"So you're saying cheating on me was just a cover up because Shawnquetta overheard us having sex?"

"Well, not entirely. I would be lyin' if I said yes and left it at that. Around that time I had a lot of things goin' on in my mind about my sexuality. I was startin' to feel bad for bein' so in love with a man, wonderin' how long I would continue to be attracted to the same sex, and wantin' it to go away because my daughter was gettin' older and I never wanted her to know about this part of me. All those thoughts runnin' through my mind and the fact that I hadn't been with a female sexually in years was really gettin' to me. I was feeling like less of a man and it seemed like Shawnquetta findin' out was the perfect time to... Well, even though I knew I still was sexually attracted to females, it seemed like a good excuse at the time to justify gettin' some. But it really wasn't worth it. If I could relive that day a thousand times, I would stay home and be with you each time. Soon, not only will Shawnquetta be robbin' me blind for money for my daughter, but it will be twice as bad for the child that's on the way."

"So do you still feel that way?"

"What way?"

"Like you don't want to be with men? Like you don't want your daughter to see that side of you, and like you don't want your family or anyone else to know."

"I don't feel like it's anybody else's business what I do. And as far as me wantin' to be with men, no, I don't want to be with *men*. I want to be with you, just you, Jayson Story. Like I said, if I could rewind time, I would change it. We would still be together and still be happy. But then again, it took me losin' you to realize how much you mean to me," he said.

"So you don't want to be straight?"

"Yes I do, but only because that would make life so much easier."

"Do you still feel the need to be with females?"

"Honestly, while we were apart I've experienced enough women to hold me over till our golden anniversary. Now, if you give me another chance and we make it 'til then… Well, let's just say on that day we will need to have a little talk." He paused with a big smile.

"So you won't ever forgive me?" he asked.

"No," I said hurriedly as I hopped into the shower.

"No, you won't or no, you will?"

"I can forgive you, but it still hurts."

"Do you think that pain will keep us from gettin' back together?"

"I don't know," I said as I turned on the shower, letting the hot water massage my tension away.

We would be back together. Hell, we were already back together judging by the way I let him keep coming by, calling and romancing me. If things continued at that pace, I knew we would be back in love in no time, and after just having the most blazing sex with him and the way my heart was now dancing around in my chest, I was almost sure that's what I wanted. But what was I going to do about Red?

16

Blackness covered everything as far as my eyes could see. I lifted my hands toward my face and could not see them until they were just about an inch away from my nose.

Silence accompanied the charcoal-colored walls of the scene. The silence was as thick as the dark world around me, leaving me completely alone with my hazy thoughts. I felt fully relaxed as I drifted in and out until reality had become just as void as the light.

And then there was illumination.

I looked around a stadium filled to capacity with what seemed to be screaming people of all ages, races and backgrounds. The people were shouting names and they were divided in half, right down the center of the large auditorium.

Half of the gigantic crowd was screaming Dorey's name over and over again and the other half were yelling out Red's name. The combination of chanting, applause and whistles created such a thunderous boom that they overwhelmed the arena.

A wave broke out, just like you would see at any large sporting event when the crowd was feeling good and full of excitement. The wave of people simultaneously standing up, throwing their hands in the air then returning to a seated position in their chairs created a human domino effect as I watched in awe.

A second closer look around the stadium revealed that though the crowd of thousands was still filled with bodies, there was a change. This time they all bore my likeness. An eerie feeling came over me as I noticed the sudden switch.

There were signs all around. Different colors and phrases adorned the posters, which said things like "Red is number one" and "Dorey is the champ." A curiously wonderful feeling filled me. I was now dying to discover what was going on and why so many people had come out in such numbers, while they cheered for the two men in my life.

Right in the center of the crowd was a boxing ring that was completely empty, with the exception of a tiny, middle-aged, white man standing in the center as a bright spotlight beamed down on him. He was short and stocky, baldheaded with a pencil-thin mustache and plain features. Dressed in heavily starched black trouser pants, a freshly pressed white shirt and bowtie, he stood in silence for a moment, looking around at the crowd. He appeared to be intimidated by its awesome size. As a microphone slowly descended from the ceiling, he shed his meek and timid exterior, revealing himself to be a professional announcer, full of confidence. After grabbing the microphone he started to speak with control that overpowered the chants and screams of the rowdy audience.

"Atlanta, Georgia, let's get ready to RUMBLE!" he said enthusiastically, igniting the already unruly crowd with even more power-packed energy. The tiny hairs on my arms were standing straight up as I, too, became filled with excitement, anticipating whatever was about to happen.

"The first competitor coming to the ring, standing five feet nine inches of deep, dark chocolate masculinity, weighing in at one hundred and seventy pounds of solid muscle with washboard abs, big, strong arms, an ass so big and tight it would make an anorexic salivate and a front package that's just as nice, full of so much sex appeal any woman, or man for that matter, would love to be with him. Here he is, the champion, Dorey, "The Heartbreaker" Braxton."

Dorey came walking toward the ring slowly, wearing a thin, black, satin robe with the word "Heartbreaker" embroidered on it. As he entered the ring, greeted the crowd and disrobed, revealing his sexy physique, he wore only a pair of the skintight, white, Calvin Klein boxer briefs I gave him on our second anniversary. Dorey knew how much I loved to see him in those underwear; he knew it turned me on more than anything. There was something almost hypnotic about seeing the contrast of the clean, white material hugging his smooth, brown skin that made my heart race.

I sat in my seat admiring Dorey's glistening body as the spotlight now shined on him. He sauntered slowly around the ring and the crowd no longer cheered, but made lustful noises and explicit comments prompting me to jealousy.

The whole crowd now sat wide-eyed and in awe with their mouths open, doe-eyed for Dorey's irresistibility.

Suddenly, Dorey's fifteen seconds of fame were up and his spotlight was dimmed before the announcer resumed control.

"Next up is the challenger!" the tiny man said while receiving 'boo's' from the crowd.

"Standing slim and toned at six feet three inches, weighing in at two hundred and five pounds, resembling a light-skinned Greek God with smooth, reddish skin, alluring, big, beautiful, light brown eyes, legs so stacked, so defined it looks like he's been running track since he was two, large strong hands that prove the theory right about large hands and a large…well, you know the rest. He's got the looks, all the right tools and knows how to work them like a professional. Hell, he is a pro! He's the pretty boy thug type you've secretly been looking for, with both brains and street smarts. He's never broken your heart and has no intentions of doing so. He only wants to love you, but you just don't see it because your heart's so calloused it has you going through life thinking you don't need anyone to love you when you know good and well you do…"

"Enough!" I screamed, giving the announcer a cold stare, letting him know that his point had been made and there was need to continue.

"Without further adieu, the challenger, Red "The *Hustler*" AKA Bryan Tymes!" The announcer said enthusiastically.

As music started to play, Red made his way through the crowd. As he walked, the people sat relatively calm, compared to the hype they displayed during Dorey's grand-entrance.

Red wore a plain, white robe with no frills. It wasn't made of any fancy material, like silk or satin, just cotton with a hood pulled up over his bowed head so you couldn't see his face while he stood motionless in the center of the ring.

Suddenly, a bouquet of a dozen, beautiful, long-stem white roses appeared in his hand as he made his way to me. He gave me a sweet, soft and innocent kiss on the forehead, and then said he loved me. Even though he spoke those words at a whisper, they seemed to boom throughout the arena.

When Red returned to the ring, he threw off his robe, revealing a white toga draped over one side of his body and showing off most of his beautiful frame. As he made his way around the ring once, he put on a seductive strip tease until he was toga-free, wearing only a pair of Timberland boots. He had his hands cupped tightly around his almost exposed masculinity, making sure the contents inside were un-shown.

Now the fickle crowd had come around and they began to cheer. Red managed to convert most of Dorey's following. How could they possibly resist the black Greek god standing before them?

Then, after all the crowd had come to the edges of their seats trying to get a better view of Red's anatomy, he threw up his hands revealing each and every inch of himself, and the crowd went wild. Pandemonium erupted; the crowd came to their feet as they gave him a standing ovation. The deafening sounds of handclaps, whistles and catcalls grew to levels that could rock Richter scales.

"And now, judging tonight's event, you all know him, and you all love him. Jay-son Sssssttttttooooorrrryyyy!" the announcer said as the spotlight turned its bright beams on me.

The light continued to grow brighter until the glowing white light was almost blinding.

I awoke with my heart racing so hard and fast it felt like it might escape my chest. I was sweaty, tense and panting heavily as I thought about the strange dream I just had.

My indecisiveness over whom I should be with had gotten to a point that it was disturbing my sleep.

"What's wrong, baby?" Dorey asked, embracing me, and then positioning my body so that my head was resting on his chest. He started to rub my head softly with his palms, wiping the sweat away.

"What's wrong?" he asked again.

"I just had a bad dream, that's all," I said.

He kissed me lightly on my cheek and caressed my body as we cuddled tightly, and then he started to drift back to sleep.

I needed some air so I got up from the bed, leaving Dorey with a surprised expression on his face as if to say "Huh?" Before he could ask, I assured him I was okay and made up an excuse about having to talk to my roommate. If I told the truth, I knew it would have only led to more questions. Questions I wasn't ready to answer.

"Jarvis, are you up?" I asked, opening his bedroom door and walking into his dimly lit bedroom. He was in bed, flipping aimlessly through channels on the television as I walked over, plopped my body down next to him and let out a huge sigh of frustration.

"What's wrong with you?" he asked.

"I am just so confused."

"About what?"

I started to tell Jarvis about the dream I had and the fact that I was torn between whether or not to give Dorey a second chance, or if I should just see where things ended up with Red.

Completely frustrated with no idea of what to do, I looked to my best friend for guidance. Maybe he could provide me with some insight, because I had no clue.

Dorey had still been calling, stopping by and spending the night. Every day that passed was a day he planted seeds of persuasion for us to work things out, leaving me torn. His constant presence made it almost impossible to think about if I should let him back in my life, because he had already placed himself in the picture without permission.

Red's arrival had given me even more to ponder. The last thing I expected was to like him, but he seemed so sincere and unique. I was finding it hard not to be drawn to him and eager to see where things could possibly go. He had stopped hustling and made many positive changes in the short time I'd known him that I knew were all for me.

"I don't know what the big deal is. I mean, it's not like you are married to either one of them. You act like it's impossible to date more than one person at a time. We are not back in the days of old where there was no such thing as casual dating. It's okay to date them both as long as you are honest," Jarvis said.

"I've never dated more than one person at a time. I don't know if…"

"Yeah, well, you are now, so just make the best of it. There is nothing wrong with getting to know people. That's the problem with dating. Everyone feels the need to rush into a premature relationship just because they think they've met someone 'special' before taking the time to find out whether or not the person is really worth the time and effort. Instead of taking things slow and getting to know one another, they rush things, leading to an inevitable breakup within the typical three-month time frame. I hate seeing all these people act like they are so in love and can't live without their latest lover. One week youre their 'boo, pookie, and baby,' you hold hands and all that other sweet shit, but then comes the breakup and they move right on to the next within a week or two, repeating the same damn cycle. That makes me sick… Oopps my fault im just venting, this isn't about me or my issues." Jarvis said.

"I've never been through that though," I said.

"I know and you should consider yourself lucky. You've never really had to date, because you were with Dorey for so long and he was the only one you've ever really been with. But let me tell you, dating is not for the faint of heart. It can be rough. Keep doing what you are doing. Don't make any promises to either one. Let them take you out and have a good time. Soon enough, you will find the answers. Maybe Dorey has changed for the better. Maybe Red is 'Mr. Right.' Only time will tell. Three months is usually enough time for most men to start showing their true colors. That. Please, please just don't go putting all your eggs in one basket, and don't go rushing into anything. Be patient."

"Okay," I said reluctantly as I buried my face in Jarvis' back, letting out another loud sigh.

"But, if you really feel the need to speed up the process, have sex with them both," he said bluntly.

"What!" I said.

"Sex will help you decide. Sex can act as an invisible magnifying glass in most relationships. See, if you hook up with Red, and it's like watching paint dry, chances are yall have uncovered issues and/or you won't be too enthused about continuing to get to know him. Lousy sex can be the ultimate turnoff. But on the other hand, if you sleep with him and the sex is spectacular, you may just forget all about Dorey."

"Oh, my God, you are retarded," I said.

"No, I'm serious. Have sex with him and then watch how much clarity you get. Just make sure you use protection cause you already know the deal."

"I'm going back to bed," I said, shaking my head with a look of disgust on my face. As I walked away, he threw his pillow at me, hitting me in the back.

Though Jarvis and I took very different views on a wide array of topics, I knew he had a point. Rushing things or stressing over what to do was the last thing I needed. Dorey and Red would just have to continue to take things at the pace

I set, keeping things strictly casual until I made up my mind on which route I should go.

Dorey was lying peacefully in a deep sleep as I returned to the room. However, the second my head hit the pillow and I slid my body down next to his, he woke up, grabbed me, kissed the back of my neck and whispered "goodnight."

Dorey was not going to make my decision easy.

17

So this is what casual sex feels like, I thought as I lay on the bed with my face buried in a pillow, providing a buffer for my moans of ecstasy. Up until that day, I had gone my whole life having sex with only one person. By the pleasure received from number two, I started to feel deprived.

My parents conditioned me to believe that you should only have sex with someone you love. Anything else was pointless and dirty. Over the years I had grown to cling to their beliefs, but tonight the way this man made my body feel was far from either pointless or dirty.

"Mmmmmmm"
"Yeah, you like that?"
"Just like that. Ooooooh, damn boy."

Laying there with Red on top of me, every touch, kiss and everything else felt sensational. Even the slightest chill from the cold air in the room sent blissful pleasure over my body. How could this feel so good? Yes, I liked Red a lot, but I was far from being in love with him. Dorey was the only man I'd ever loved, and with him the sex felt equally as good as the sensual sex with Red. So I guess I was dispelling the myth my parents instilled in me about sex and love.

It was the kind of lovemaking people write songs about, laced with just enough hot sex thrown in that I was getting loud enough for my neighbors to call the police. I enjoyed every moment as we disturbed the peace, going at it for hours.

"Hell yeah!"

"What? You want that?"

"Mmmmm, yeah, that's what I want baby, give it to me."

"How do you want it, boy?"

"Oooh shit! Just like that!"

He caressed my lower stomach with his goatee, seductively moving the hairs in a circular motion around my navel with just the right amount of pressure to make my back arch and toes curl. I gently began to rub his silky-feeling hair, and then gave his head a light shove, letting him know right where I wanted him to be. He looked up at me with wide, passionate eyes and said "Baby, I got you." I let Red resume control, hoping he would go there soon. We had explored almost every inch of each other's bodies that night, but not once had he put his mouth on my sex. Although I was thoroughly enjoying everything else, once he did that, it would be like the icing on my favorite cake.

Seconds later, I felt a warm sensation just short of incredible move over me and as I closed my eyes, I fell into a supernatural state.

"Gotdayum that feels good!"

"Oh you like that?"

"Uh-huh."

The lovemaking took me to another place both physically and mentally until suddenly I felt nothing and the room grew silent. When I opened my eyes to see what halted the flow, I saw Red standing over me glistening, covered with glossy beads of perspiration.

"Follow me," he said, tossing my clothes at me and helping me up from the bed.

"What the...?" I asked under my breath, baffled by the sudden change of events. I struggled to get my underwear and pants up over my still aroused lower organ. Red threw on his clothes, grabbed my hand and said, "Don't worry. Just come with me."

He led me outside of the apartment then instructed me to hop on his back, close my eyes and not open them till he told me.

"This probably looks so gay," I said.

"I don't care and neither should you," he replied.

"Open," he instructed as he lowered me down to the ground, and I noticed that he had brought me to a secluded spot in a wooded area of the apartment complex. There in our private place, he had prepared a blanket and some pillows.

I smiled intensely, wondering what Red had up his sleeve, though it didn't take long to find out. He started kissing me with the heat and fire of burning wildfire. A few seconds later, we were both naked again, going at each other while the sounds of insects buzzed around us.

"You feel so good, better than I imagined," Red said as he started to find himself inside my body.

It took everything I had to keep quiet. Every now and then I had to let verbal emotions escape, which broke the calm of the night. Then Red would cover my mouth with his hand while he continued to do his thing from the back, hitting all the right spots.

Our bodies united, as we moved in a simultaneous back-and-forth motion. Red's hands sweetly attacked my naked skin. He took them, grabbed my waist tightly and pulled my body firmly into his, released it slightly, then continued that same rhythm several times. I knew I was coming close to my peak. By the noises Red had began to make after being relatively quiet, and by the way his body had begun to buckle, I knew he was getting close, too.

"Oh shit, mmmm. Damn!"

Red paused for a minute then took time to explore me with his hands again, moving in close. When he got to my face, he grabbed it and kissed me slowly and deeply, which felt almost as good as the sex inside me. A rush surged through my body as our tongues danced seductively in each others' mouths.

Red rolled my body over until I was laying flat on my back.

He pulled my legs up slowly into the air, and then swiftly placed himself back inside me as our legs became one, resembling a human x, and he went even deeper.

Red and I both could no longer keep quiet. I let out a passionate moan that was followed by Red's quivering vibrato, groaning as he let me know how good I felt.

"Damn, boy, that ass feels so good."

"You like that?"

"Nah, baby, I'm lovin' that ass."

"Yeah, take that shit."

We went from a slow and long stroking motion, gradually building momentum as each moment passed until we found ourselves pumping our bodies as fast as we both could take. He was moving his body up and down over me in a vigorous motion as I threw my body back at him, and a sweat broke out across his forehead.

"Yeah, just like that," I said.

"Ohhh," was the only thing Red could manage in response.

I gazed lustfully into his big, brown eyes, reading his thoughts. I knew without him saying a word that the pleasure I was giving was so good that it was too much. I could tell that at any moment, his body was going to succumb to the power and rapture.

Seeing his pleasure was turning me on so much that soon I realized the uncontrollable twitches of my body, followed by the involuntary loss of focus, and the pressure I felt building inside, were my own indication that I was close to my finale.

"Damn, baby, I'm close," Red said.

"Me, to-oooo. Oh, hell yeah." I said, barely able to speak the words.

Then, after just a few more enjoyable seconds, a little more dirty talk, and a couple moans, the end of our night of passion arrived. Red and I came together with simultaneous sighs of elation.

"Damn!" Red said.

With one word there was a change in the entire atmosphere. That word wasn't like the other "damns" he'd uttered all night long. He said it like something was terribly wrong, which made my body switch from the elevated high that a climax brings to cutting the bliss short so that I could focus on what was wrong.

"What's wrong?" I asked, opening my eyes.

I noticed he was looking down with a shocked and apologetic look. My eyes followed his to see what he was staring at, but I didn't see anything odd.

"What's wrong?" I asked again.

"I'm sorry J. I didn't mean…" he said, as I felt him growing limp, losing the wonderful erection that had brought us both so much contentment and he began to pull out from his place inside of me.

"I'm sorry," Red said again.

I didn't know why he was apologizing. The sex was spectacular; I couldn't have asked for more. Why had he all of a sudden become so thrown?

Red got up, looked at me without saying another word, and then picked up something, holding it in his hands.

"What's that?" I asked, still tragically clueless.

Red opened up his hand and dangled the item he had been holding. The black, latex condom we used to protect ourselves had broken and was in shreds, resembling more of a black rubber band and a broken balloon. That was the first time anything like that had happened to me. I wasn't sure if it was the roughness of our sex, if the condom was too small for Red, or if it was just defective. All I knew was that it being broken was bad.

I was horrified. The condom had burst, which meant that Red had cum inside of me. All of the people Red had sex with and all of his possible sexual encounters filled my mind, making me feel dirty and scared.

Taking my hand and placing it around my backside, all I felt was wetness. Was it Red's remains, the lubrication we had used, or a mixture of the two?

"Oh, my God," I said, feeling panicked.

I grabbed my clothes, quickly putting my underwear back on, and without taking time to put on the rest of my clothes. I made a quick exit as I heard Red apologizing again. I started running as fast as I could back to my apartment.

"Damn it!" I said as I beat my fist against the bathroom wall. "Damn it! Damn it! Damn it! How the hell could I have let this happen?"

I continued to talk to myself. Even though I knew the condom had broken already and the damage was done, I still thought of things I could do to try and reverse what had taken place, or at least do something that would put my mind at ease.

The thought of AIDS came with violence. I thought about the people I knew who either had HIV or had died from AIDS and how I vowed never to let it happen to me. All the faces of people I had known who contracted the virus came flashing before my eyes and a hopeless feeling surfaced while I cringed at the fact that I may very well be next. Thinking about the pneumonia, the lesions, the night sweats and the emaciated state in which I had seen people dying of AIDS terrified me.

I got down on my knees right there on the bathroom floor and started praying like some spirit-filled evangelist at a church revival, crying out to God and asking Him to come save me. I apologized to the Lord for seeming to call Him only when I was in despair and promised that I would be a much better man if He would only get me out of the situation okay.

I made a vow that if I was lucky enough not to get HIV, I would start going back to church and change a lot of my ways. I said so many things and was talking so fast that I could barely keep up with myself. By the time I had said

"Amen" and opened my eyes, I had forgotten that I was on the bathroom floor of my apartment and not at church in front of the altar.

As I got up from my knees, I felt a little better, but I was still scared of the possibility that after one night of mind-blowing sex, I may have subjected myself to so many horrible things.

I turned on the faucet in the shower, making the water as high and hot as it could go, and the bathroom quickly filled with a cloud of steam. Taking long deep breaths of the hot cloudy air calmed me and helped me relax as I devised a plan.

I got an enema from the medicine cabinet then proceeded to thoroughly cleanse myself. After the first time, I filled it with lukewarm water from the bathroom sink and just kept on washing out my insides until I felt I had done it enough to get anything and everything that may have been in there out. True, I wasn't a doctor and what I was doing may have been in vain, or have done more harm than good, but it made me feel better.

After I finished, I turned the temperature on the shower down to a point where it was no longer scalding, but just blazing enough to wash without burning myself.

I must have stayed in that shower for at least an hour, until every drop of hot water was absorbed. I had washed my body from head to toe with the soapy washcloth at least a dozen times, leaving no crevice unclean. I even drenched the rag in rubbing alcohol a few times for good measure, thinking that would kill every germ.

When I was done, I dried myself and went to my room, where I crawled, naked, under the covers in and picked up the phone to call Red. I felt the need to apologize for freaking out and explain why I ran off in such a hurry. Even though I knew he probably already knew the reason I had acted so crazy, I still wanted to say I was sorry.

Instead of his voice, I heard was an automated voice telling me the number I was trying to reach had been disconnected.

"Oh, well," I said, assuming Red had not paid his phone bill and that I would catch up with him once his phone was back on or he called me, whichever came first.

My health became my main concern.

18

"Hello, and how can I assist you today?" the friendly looking teller with a wide, artificial smile said from behind the half wall-and-glass partition separating us.

"Hi, I would like to make a withdrawal," I said, slipping the small piece of paper that contained my name and savings account information on it under the glass.

Normally, I would just use my credit card, debit card, or a check to cover all of my monetary needs. However, losing my wallet was a major inconvenience; turning many simple things into long, drawn-out procedures that made me wish I hadn't been so absentminded.

The minute things started getting even remotely hectic, my mind became a blur and I started misplacing things. Almost anything that wasn't attached to me could be lost during those times of chaos, and sometimes I felt like I was losing myself.

Standing there watching as the teller typed my information onto her computer with lightning-fast speed, effortlessly stroking the keyboard. I was amazed by the fact that her smile had not changed its position. That smile was still just as fixed as it had been when I first saw her and could not be genuine. No one could be that happy to be at work.

While waiting for my money, I stood there looking around the bank's posh interior as the line quickly grew behind me. The bank resembled an old-world English parlor with its fancy tapestries, deep mahogany wood furniture and warm lighting.

The gentile spirited, smiley-faced teller who had seemed so nice and polite all of a sudden didn't seem so kind. She told me something I never heard before and never thought I would have to hear.

If she would have taken the computer's monitor, picked it up, and then dropped it on my head, that probably would have felt better than hearing the words she uttered.

"I'm sorry, Mr. Story. I will not be able to give you any money back with this transaction. Your account is currently overdrawn."

"There's got to be some kind of mistake," I said boldly, confident that lately my account was never without at least a few hundred dollars of emergency cash, just in case something came up. What this lady was telling me couldn't be true.

All I was trying to get was fifty measly dollars. However, Brenda the teller was telling me that I didn't have anything in my account. She must have been new and typed in something wrong. There had to be some kind of mistake.

"Can you check that again? And are you sure you have the right account pulled up?" I asked calmly, trying not to get myself upset until she verified that it was in fact the correct information.

"Jayson Story?" she asked.

"Yes," I replied.

"And can you verify the last four digits of your social security number for me, please?"

"2153."

"Well, the information I have is correct and I'm showing that your account is overdrawn by $540," she continued softly.

"*What?!*" I demanded. "How could this be?"

"Sir, if you would kindly have a seat over in the waiting area, someone will be with you momentarily."

I took a deep breath as my body temperature began to simmer. There was a knot full of tension forming between my eyes as I felt my blood pressure rise. One thing I couldn't play with was my money. With the news that I was not only broke but in debt, I felt as if my life was going to steer itself out of control again and that just couldn't happen.

As I sat in the waiting area in the midst of a handful of other customers who were also waiting to be helped, suddenly I grew paranoid. It felt like everyone's eyes were on me as they secretly laughed, pointed and talked about me behind my back.

I placed the palm of my hand on my forehead and bowed my head trying to disappear into my lap. I wanted to cry. The last thing I needed was to be broke in the midst of everything else that was going on in my life. The tension headache I was experiencing built as I continued to wait.

"Mr. Story," a voice said at the very same time I felt a hand touch me gently on the shoulder.

I looked up to notice a rather attractive, white female standing about 5'9", fully made up with glossy, dark blond hair pulled back in a bun. She looked like a model fresh off the pages of *Vogue* or *Cosmopolitan*, wearing a long, figure-hugging black skirt, black high heels and white-striped silk blouse, which wrapped around her waist. After greeting me with a half smile, she instructed me to follow her. As I trailed her, I could smell the scent of vanilla and jasmine lingering in the air. Then, she motioned me to go in her office. Following me, she closed the door and took a seat at her large, mahogany desk.

"The reason we requested you come back to my office today is because your account has some sensitive information on it."

"Yes, the previous representative informed me that my account is overdrawn. There must be some sort of error because I keep records of all my transactions and I have never had insufficient funds in my life. I have more than enough money in the account to cover anything that may take place, so this…" I hesitated then continued, trying to sound as professional as I could. "This just cannot be!"

"I assure you, Mr. Story, this is no error. You may want to double-check any records you have and get back to me. Here's my card," she said while retrieving the card from her fancy business card holder sitting on the corner of her desk.

She stared back at her computer screen for a moment before quickly hitting a few buttons on her keyboard to print out a copy of my records. She handed me a few sheets of paper that listed my daily transactions from the current month.

"Your account has been frozen due to the excessive negative balance you've accumulated and it will remain frozen until your account is brought current."

The woman seated before me, who at first glance was quite a beauty, had quickly become an ugly, old hag. I couldn't believe her words. Nothing like this had ever happened to me. How did this happen? Since I had lost my wallet, I hadn't made any purchases with anything other than cash. But there I was, holding these sheets of paper full of charges to my bankcard I had no recollection of, to many places I had never even been.

Then it hit me. Not one time did I think until that very moment that someone may have found my wallet and had been using the information it contained to go on a shopping spree, courtesy of me. I had lost my wallet half a dozen times before, but never had this happened. Every other time, I would always find my wallet within a few days, after retracing my steps. But obviously this time was different. This time, someone found my wallet and decided to live it up on my dime.

"Oh, I just remembered, Ms. Randal," I said taking a moment to look at the business card she had given me. "I lost my wallet a few weeks ago. I hadn't bothered to call to cancel my cards and checks because I'm always misplacing my wallet only to find it again a couple of days later. That's what brought me into the bank today actually. I came to withdraw…" I said, suddenly cut off by Ms. Randal before I could finish.

"Mr. Story, it is your responsibility to call and notify the bank as soon as you realize you have a lost or stolen bankcard or checks. That way we are able to put notes on the account, which are to the advantage of our customers in a situation such as this. When that occurs, the customer is not liable for any charges made to their account *after* an alert has been posted. This is all explained in the terms and conditions you signed when you opened your account," she stated, in staccato fashioned words.

"Didn't you receive the calls or notices we've sent in the mail?"

"Honestly I thought the calls were telemarketers and the mailings were just junk." I said.

"Well they weren't."

Her words, and the way she chose to say them, put me on the defensive. I became upset by the fact that she was talking down to me, like I was a child incapable of holding an adult conversation.

"Ms. Randal, there is no need to insult my intelligence. I fully understand what you are saying without you sounding out everything phonetically."

I felt the tension in my body elevating to even higher levels. If this matter was not resolved within the next few minutes, there were two things that were bound to happen. One, I would become livid and surely raise hell in the office, or two, become livid and surely raise hell in the office.

"Mr. Story, I understand that you may be upset, but there is no need for you to take that tone of voice," she said condescendingly.

"Tone? What tone?" I demanded. "Are you referring to the *same* tone in which you've been speaking to me?"

Ms. Randal said nothing, just sat there with a half-blank, half-pissed-off-but-not-trying-to-show-it look across her heavily made up face. I was itching for the once prim and proper white lady to get ghetto by rolling her eyes, shaking her head or pointing her finger at me so I could really have just cause to snap. However, I didn't get my wish. She just sat there staring silently at me. Though her voice made no sound her eyes read, "So what do you expect *me* to do about this? *My* account *has* money in it!"

After a few moments of awkward silence, Ms. Randal's voice cut the stillness. "I'm sorry about the inconvenience. Is there anything else I can assist you with?" The reflections of her voice still hadn't changed; she sounded even more arrogant and condescending than ever.

"Yes, there is something you can do for me. You can let me speak to a manager!" I demanded.

"Mr. Story, I am a manager."

"Okay, well, since I got absolutely nowhere with you, how about you let me speak to the branch manager, and if he or she can't help me, then I'll need to speak to *their* manager and so on and so forth until I get all the way to your corporate office, if that's what it takes to get this resolved. I've banked with this company since I was a child. Surely there is something that can be done in this situation other than freezing my account and holding me liable for charges that I did not make."

"Here you are, Mr. Story. This is the card of the branch manager, Mr. Anthony Pettis. He's out of the office today, but he will be back in on Monday."

"Thank you," I said, taking the card, still annoyed by Ms. Randal's lack of compassion and terrible attitude. I could tell I had gotten to her because her face was rosy red and it was showing even through all the layers of her foundation.

"Good day, Ms. Randal, and thanks for *all* your help," I said sarcastically as I exited her office and proceeded to leave the bank.

On the way home, I took out my cell phone and called Jarvis. I needed to tell him about what I had just encountered. Maybe talking to him about this and venting a little would help me release some tension.

"You would not believe the news I just got," I said.

"Let me guess, you won the lottery and you're calling because you want to give your best friend in the world half."

"Nope, but it's ironic you would say that because it's actually quite the opposite. I'm flat broke, but you are welcome to share half of nothing with me," I said.

"Huh? Broke? I thought you were saving rainy day money since you moved back?" he asked.

"Well, I have been, but I just left the bank and they informed me that not only am I broke, I'm in the negatives. I owe them over five hundred dollars, mostly overdraft charges for purchases I didn't even make. They've placed a hold on my account and basically told me not to even think about trying to touch my account until I give them theirs," I said.

"So I guess you know what happened to your wallet," he said.

"Yeah, I guess I didn't just lose it. Someone must have stolen it and racked up all of these charges on my account."

"Yeah, and I bet I know who it was," Jarvis said.

"Who?" I asked.

"That low down mutha fukka, *Red*. I never did like him. Just think, the night you met him was the same night you called looking for your wallet, and now you haven't heard from him in weeks after he was acting damn near in love with you. *It's obvious*," he said.

"Huh? *You*, were the one who convinced me to go out with him in the first place, and I really don't think he did it."

Jarvis ignored my comments and continued on, unfazed.

"I mean, think about it, Jayson. He's a hustler. They do shit like this all the time. Consider yourself lucky, because I've heard some stories that are a lot worse," he said.

"No, I don't think he would do something like that."

"Don't be so naïve, Jayson. You really didn't know much about him, so you don't know what he is or isn't capable of."

"Yeah, but..." I continued defending Red for a moment until I started closely reviewing the dates and charges on my bank statement, noticing that they were made the same time Red had come into the picture. Suddenly, a few of the charges started looking familiar. I had to pull my car over on the side of the highway so that I could take an even closer look.

11-20 Minks Package Store $20.40

11-20 Hillard's Flowers $27.99

11-20 Rich's Department Store $109.79

That was the same day that Red and I first officially met for our "date" and it hit me. Red had used my card to buy the flowers, the wine and the nice new clothes he was wearing.

"Oh, my God, I feel so stupid," I said. In my disbelief I reluctantly realized that Red was really the culprit.

He'd seemed so genuinely interested in me that I would have never pegged him to be a liar or a thief. But, there the proof was, right before my eyes in bold print. It was undeniable.

Stealing from me was low, but giving me stolen things paid for with my own money took the situation to a whole new world of lowness.

"It's not your fault. He was a hustler, *period.* You had no way of knowing this would happen," Jarvis said, trying to consol me.

"Yeah, he was a hustler in more ways than one. I guess that's what I get for being so damn dumb. But does every man I allow myself to like have to fuck me over so bad?"

"It will be okay, Jay. Soon you will be a world-famous author and you won't even need money. But in the meantime, you may want to get a copy of your credit report and check it from time to time to make sure Red hasn't done any further damage," Jarvis said, as I merged back onto the highway and drove my newly broke self home.

19

My whole body was trembling and covered with a thin film of perspiration. It felt as if someone was chasing me and the only way to get away with my life was to run. Running away felt like the only natural and logical thing to do at the moment. The only thing was, no one was after me and there was no danger that needed escaping, other than the danger of my past, which was irreversible.

Standing still and frozen in the waiting room at Atlanta's Outreach, a clinic which gave free and anonymous STD prevention and treatment services, I kept debating weather I should follow through with things. Would it be wise for me to stay and subject myself to this torment? In my present state of ignorance, was it truly bliss? Would knowing be better than remaining uncertain? And if I chickened out would the uncertainty of possibly having an STD eventually drive me crazy?

Before I had time to figure things out or answer all the questions sifting through my mind, my name was called.

"Jay…Jay Briggs." I heard a female voice calling out. Had it not been for me being the only person in the waiting room, I would have almost forgotten that I was being called because of the alias I had jotted down on the sign-in sheet.

"Hi, Jay. I'm Dr. Kline," said the lady whose polished appearance and features bared a striking resemblance to Oprah Winfrey as she shook my hand and told me to follow her.

It felt like she was marching me to meet my fate in front of a judge and jury after committing one of the worlds most heinous crimes. It was too late to turn around now. Each step felt like it took an eternity.

Everything was going in slow motion with the exception of my heart. The heavy thuds of my heartbeat crashed violently against the walls of my chest like an unstable ton of bricks. Briefly pausing for a moment to take a much-needed deep breath, I inhaled and exhaled as a big rush of wind fled my lungs, helping to release some tension. The audible exhale caught Dr. Kline's attention.

Sensing my worry, Dr. Kline grabbed me softly, put her arm in mine, and tried to comfort me by telling me that everything was okay. Her matronly way consoled me and soothed my doubts as we finished walking to her office.

"So, Jay, what brings you here today?" Dr. Kline asked.

"I'm here for an HIV test," I said softly.

"I take it that this is your first time," she said.

"Yes," I said barely managing to get it out over the knot in my throat.

She began to talk me through what I should expect and gave me some general information about AIDS and HIV. Then as she pulled out a sheet of paper with questions filling every inch of its surface and our meeting quickly became a lot more personal.

"Since 1981 have you ever had sex with a male?" she asked matter-of-factly.

I was so unprepared for that question. It was probably routine for her to ask that same question to everyone who walked into her clinic, but it was abnormal for me to hear someone ask me such a frank question about my sexuality. Before I could weigh my options between telling the truth and lying, out came the truth like a rushing wind.

"Yes," I said.

My answer didn't even seem to faze Dr. Kline as she continued with her questionnaire.

"And what is your sexual orientation? Gay, straight or bisexual?" she asked.

"Gay," I said as she continued on with questions, not showing even the slightest signs of hatred or judgment. I wasn't at all used to just coming out and admitting what I did behind closed doors, but today was different. Dr. Kline asking me how I got down wasn't like someone off the street asking me if I was gay. She was asking for a reason and I figured it was to complete her questionnaire effectively. The truth wouldn't hurt either one of us.

After the questions ended, I felt comfortable enough with her to open up even more. She asked if there was anything in particular that brought me in to get tested.

Without hesitation, I gave her the abridged version of my one-night stand with Red, how the condom burst, and how I had been full of worry and guilt ever since. Dr. Kline was really down to earth and told jokes that helped lighten the mood and I tried to do the same. Without passing judgment, she listened to every word and kept reassuring me that, no matter what, everything was going to be okay.

"Jay, you are way too young and attractive to be stressing so hard. Leave the stressing to old folks like me who know how to do it right."

Then with a little laugh came the moment I had been fearing.

Dr. Kline opened up a sealed packet and pulled out what looked like a long Q-tip with a small, flat, rectangular head. She instructed me to place it between my lower gum and cheek for five minutes. I placed the salty swab in my mouth and could almost hear the silent second hand on the clock ticking in my ear.

We continued to shoot the breeze until the timer went off. She then took the swab, placed it in a clear tube, sealed it, wrote some numbers on it, placed it in an envelope and put the envelope in a bin that said "outgoing mail." She told me that it would be a week until I could come back to get my results and gave me a business card with the name and number of the clinic on it, along with a long number that corresponded with my test information.

After she was done administering the test, she continued taking the time to get to know me. It seemed like she really wanted to know me for some reason and that she wasn't just asking questions because it was her job. In fact the conversation had passed professional just as soon as she removed the swab from my mouth. She said I reminded her of her godson and hinted that maybe one day I might like to come to her house for dinner and meet him.

No, Dr. Kline was not trying to hook me up with her godson, I thought, while listening to her go on and on about how similar we were and how much I would like him. I politely declined the potential hookup, letting her know that I had way too many issues to take on another potential mate, but was more than open to friendship.

"I could tell you had a lot on your mind when I first met you. Do you pray?" Dr. Kline asked.

"Not as much as I should," I said with shame.

"No one ever does, but you may want to try it more," she said.

Her words reminded me of my pact with God that night while on my knees on the bathroom floor and how I vowed to be so much better, but I still had made no changes.

"Another thing you may want to try is writing your emotions on paper, you know, like a journal of sorts. That's what works for me. When things get a little bit harder than I care for them to, I just get to writing and it helps calm my nerves," she said.

"Believe it or not, I used to do that. I used to write all the time. I've just been so busy lately that I haven't taken the time to. That's sad because writing is one of my greatest loves. Actually, I have a book coming out soon and I will definitely bring you an autographed copy if you want."

"Well, well. You're a writer? Congratulations! I can't wait to read it. See, I knew you were an outstanding young man. I don't just invite any old body to my home for dinner and surely not to meet my godson. Something told me your were special," she exclaimed.

Just then my cell phone rang. Dorey's number was displayed on the caller ID and I quickly sent the call straight to voicemail. I had been trying to avoid him after an argument we had over money.

It turned out that not only did Red run through all of the money that was in my bank account, he also managed to deplete the funds from the joint account that Dorey and I had set up a few years back. Once I found that out, I was more embarrassed than anything and I promised Dorey that I would make everything okay if he could just gave me a little bit of time.

Dorey wasn't pressed for the money, but the fact that it was gone because of me was enough to bring my current relationship with him to avoidance. Once the mess with the bank cleared up, which would be very soon, we could go back to normal.

"That's part of my issues there," I said still looking at my phone before getting up to leave.

On my way out, she stopped me and took the card from my hand before writing her number on the back and telling me that if I ever needed anything not to hesitate to call her. She also told me that she had connections with some people who may be able to help with my book. I thanked Dr. Kline and walked out thinking of things to do to occupy my time and take my mind off of what would be one of the longest weeks in my life.

I prayed that waiting for my HIV status would not overtake me and that the results of the test would be as pleasant as the actual test with Dr. Kline.

20

When I arrived home from the clinic, I did my daily walk to the mailbox to see if anything was waiting for me other than bills. After checking, I found that there was a letter from home. It had been so long since my mother had written me a letter because after our heart to heart when I went back home, she started calling on a much more frequent basis making letters unnecessary. I began to open the letter as I walked back to the apartment but was interrupted before I had a chance to read the first line.

Mr. Braxton was waiting for me. I should have known that I could only avoid him for so long before being forced to deal with him face to face.

"Jay, what the hell is wrong with you?"

"What are you talking about, Dorey?"

"Please don't do this. Don't act like you don't know that you have been completely avoidin' me lately without even givin' me a clue as to why. Just when I thought we were gettin' somewhere, you pull another disappearin' act. Now, when I call you don't answer and when I stop by you don't open the door. What is up?"

"I've just been really busy, that's all."

"Busy with what? And so busy that you couldn't even give me a return phone call after all this time?"

"Well, honestly our last phone call left me not wanting to call you until I was sure everything at the bank was straight so we wouldn't have to argue about the same thing twice."

"Baby, I'm sorry about getting' upset over the missin' money, but you have to admit I had a reason to be just a little upset. It wasn't even that big of a deal though. You know I've never been pressed for money. I just wanted to know what was goin' on."

"Well, from the way you came at me I sure couldn't tell it was no big deal."

"Again, Jay, I apologize. Okay?"

"It's cool. And just so you know, everything should be cleared up within the next couple of days. I've been speaking to the branch manager at the bank and he assured me that everything would be okay."

"Good! Honestly the real reason I got so upset over the money was because I was going to use what was in that account and put it toward the down payment on a house and surprise you like I did with the apartment. I wanted to show you that I was really serious about us and that I want to start a new life with you."

His words took the wind from my body and left me breathless. Buying a home was a huge step and his propositional leap of faith was one I really wasn't sure I wanted to take.

"You were going to do what?" I asked just to make sure I'd heard him correctly. Though sweet and random acts of kindness were a part of Dorey's repertoire, buying a home was a shocking undertaking, even for him.

"You heard me right, buy a house. I was also goin' to do this," he said as he started lowering his body down to the black asphalt parking lot and my body grew weaker. "Baby, I'm tired of hidin' and tired of lyin', to myself and everybody else. The truth is, before you, nothin' else in my life really mattered but Jasmine. My family, friends and everyone else can't compare to what you give me, and I need you in my life forever."

A blue box concealing a shiny, platinum band was slowly revealed and I stood speechless, baffled by what I then realized was an unstoppable happening. Never in my wildest fantasies would I have dreamed a day like that. There before me was the only man I've ever loved, down on one knee. Before I was able to fully grab hold of reality he'd already done it.

Since I hadn't been keeping up with current events and the seesaw -like drama surrounding same-sex marriages, I wasn't really sure if what he was asking me was legal, but that sure didn't stop the words from shooting from his mouth like cupid's arrow did to my heart when I first fell in love with him.

"Marry me, Jay!" he exclaimed, and I felt as if my heart would malfunction.

As he stood there waiting for one short word from me composed of three letters---Y-E-S that usually was so easy to say,--the word he anxiously awaited temporarily escaped my vocabulary.

Still in silence, my calloused core started to soften and my eyes watered. I wanted to cling to the resentment I harbored for Dorey. When I was mad at him, it was easier for me to feel better about treating him badly. But when he did sweet things for me in spite of my sometimes-stinging dis-position, it made loving him irresistible. Even with all the wrong he'd done, in that moment, I wanted to erase every shred of hurt from my memory and say "yes" so I could restart a life with him, but my better judgment said "no."

"I just need some time to think about this. You know I love you and what you've done is incredible, but you have overwhelmed me. I need a little bit of time to think."

"You need time, but I need for you to say you will and I need you in my life. But if time is what you need, I will give you that. Just know that I love you and I will be waiting for you," he said, unable to camouflage his disappointment.

Dorey's proposal had taken all of my attention from anything else and left my head spinning. In my astonishment I had forgotten about my mail from earlier. Maybe my mother would have some exciting things to share, which would take my mind off of the crucial decision I would be making very shortly.

I finished opening the letter and quickly realized that it wasn't my mother's handwriting.

––––––––––––––

Jayson,

A father's job is a hard one and you will never understand a father's mind until you have children of your own.

My job was to love you, provide for you, protect you, and raise you to be a strong man, so that you could one day face the world alone. I loved you, protected you and provided for you, but still I feel I failed as a parent.

When you were born I was so proud to have a son. Everyone could see the unmistakable joy that only a son could give his father. When you were growing up, that happiness continued and you were the mini version of me. You looked like me, acted like me, and reminded me of myself. But as you reached an age where you took on your own personality and started shaping your own destiny. You became less like me, and more of a stranger with strange ways. I wasn't prepared for the change I saw in you and though I felt you slipping away I didn't know what to do.

The day I found out that you were confused, my heart broke. I'm sorry for hitting you the way that I did. But when my worst fear for your life came true, it left me feeling like there was no choice.

Somewhere along the line I messed things up so bad we don't even speak. I know I've hurt you in ways that are inexcusable. I've said terrible things, did terrible things and as a result lost you.

Maybe we can start over. I'm not saying that it will be easy to accept you, because honestly I hate the fact that you are confused. But, I am willing to try because you are my son and though love may sometimes grow weak, a father's love never dies.

Dad

If there were any more shocking revelations that day was secretly storing, I would surely have to be committed.

21

"Hello, can I speak to Mr. Story-Braxton?"

"Shut up you idiot," I said regretting the fact that I told Jarvis about my shocking marriage proposal, but as my best friend, it was impossible to keep something that huge from him. And my valiant efforts to keep the platinum engagement ring hidden were futile because Jarvis had a sixth sense for sniffing out expensive things.

"What are you up to tonight?" he asked.

I could tell by the sound of Jarvis' voice that he was up to something. It was sneaky-sounding, like he had un-covered schemes in the works, but knowing him so well, it was apparent.

"Working. What's up with you?" I asked.

"I need you to do me a favor," he begged.

"Okay. What is it?"

"If you have any plans for tonight, drop them because I am taking you out. You know, soon you will be a married man and I probably won't be able to hang with you anymore. You know how people get once they tie that knot."

"Tonight? Well, damn, Jarvis. Thanks for the notice."

"No need to thank me. That's why I'm calling you now. This will give you more than enough time to get your mind right for tonight and be ready to go by ten o'clock, which is when we are leaving, by the way. You get off at five and it's only three now, so how much more notice could you possibly need?"

"Yeah, yeah. Where are we going?"

"I will talk to you more about that when you get home."

"What?" I asked.

"Well, talk to you later. I have to get back to work, my supervisor is coming and you know I'm not supposed to be on the phone," Jarvis said as he hung up.

"Okay, okay! I'm taking you to meet my friend, Will." Jarvis finally gave in, telling me our secret destination.

I had been begging him to no avail ever since I had come home from work to tell me the secret place he was taking me.

"Please don't tell me you got my hopes up. Not to mention the fact that I got dressed up thinking you were taking me some place interesting, only to find you are taking me to meet another one of your *many* dates," I said in disappointment.

"Well, sorry that I let you down. However, the reason I didn't tell you until now was because I knew if I did you wouldn't want to go, so I had to use a little trickery," he said.

"Well, you are right about that. You are a trick and you're damn right I wouldn't want to go," I snapped.

"It's too late now. You're going, so relax," he said.

"What's so special about this one that you want me to meet him? Usually your men come and go like faceless thumps in the night. You only let me meet the special ones."

"Will is a nice guy. I like him. Besides, I thought this outing would do you good. You need to get out of the house more. You've been so stressed out over the book, Dorey, your dad, your money, and probably a million other things running around in that crazy little skull of yours, that you haven't made any time for yourself."

"Whatever Jarvis! "

I still hadn't told Jarvis all the details regarding the situation I had gone through with Red. He knew about my wallet being stolen and we mutually came to the conclusion that Red was Mr. Sticky Fingers, but I still hadn't shared anything else about our very brief courtship. I couldn't bring myself to talk about what happened during our one-night-stand. It wasn't having sex with Red that I was ashamed of; it was the broken condom and constant fear of having HIV that kept me so secretive.

My test results hadn't come back yet, and after talking with Dr. Kline, I learned that it could take up to six months for HIV to show up in my system. That is why I couldn't bring myself to discuss the situation candidly with anyone except Dr. Kline, not even my best friend, not yet. And as far as me stressing over Dorey, the book and my Father's apology, that was all true. Jarvis was one hundred percent accurate.

"How long have you known this *Will*?"

"About a month or two now. I haven't been keeping track."

"Wow, that's almost long enough to be thinking about marriage for you. Maybe we can have a double wedding. No wonder you're taking me to meet him," I teased.

"Yeah, he is good to me."

"Where did you meet him?"

"Where else?"

"Jarvis, I told you about meeting all these people on the Internet. You have to be careful."

"*You* are telling *me* to be careful, Mr. Red? *I* am careful."

"Anyway, what side of town does he live?"

"Out in Lithonia."

"Damn, that's kind of far. I guess you don't mind the commute"

"No, I don't mind at all, especially since he's usually the one making it."

"You mean he actually drives all the way from Lithonia just to see you? He really is special then."

"Whatever!" he said laughing.

"And where was I all the times he came to see you?"

"We mostly go out, but he *has* been to the apartment several times. Each time he came, you were locked up in your room, either working on that book or sleeping like a sixty-year-old retiree."

"Yeah, well, this book is really all I have right now, and is it wrong that I want it to be a success?"

"Blah, blah, blah. Save it, old man," Jarvis said as he took his hand and placed it over my mouth attempting to silence me.

"Focus on the road, dummy!" I demanded as his actions led to the car swerving slightly into the next lane.

"So what are you gonna do about your dad?"

"You know I have no idea. He seems for real. But after everything he's done, how can I move past those things and expect to have a real father/son relationship?"

"I can see where you're coming from. You really have a lot to think about."

"Call me crazy, but even after everything we've been through, I can't hate him. I've tried to hate him, and I have every right to, but I can't."

"There aren't many times that I'm at a loss for words, but now is one of them. I can't imagine being in your shoes. Luckily I have parents who accept me no matter what. Even if I were to dye my hair green and move to Peru to be a boat salesman they would support me one hundred percent. Had I had parents like yours, well I don't know if I would have been as strong as you he-man."

"Yeah lucky you," I said as the car grew silent.

When we finally pulled up to Will's house, I did a brief double take. Were we at the right house? I sat in the car looking around at the beautiful neighborhood until Jarvis confirmed that we were at the right place when he told me to get out of the car so he could lock the door. He sensed that I was caught off guard by the extravagance as he gave me a gloating look as if he wanted to say, 'Yes, this is my boyfriend's house and you *must* be jealous!'

Will's home was in one of the better parts of Lithonia, a city located about fifteen miles outside the heart of Atlanta. The neighborhood looked like a place where you would expect to see an infestation of well-established professionals. It seemed to be a virtual melting pot of doctors, lawyers and any other line of work bringing in at least a six-figure salary.

With only one glance at the outside of his home, I was amazed and slightly disheartened. Jarvis' boyfriend was living in *my* dream home, the same house I had seen in magazines like *Home and Garden* and secretly wished for, the same home I could work hard and save my entire life for, yet still probably never be able to afford.

I was a little jealous that Jarvis always ended up dating the kind of men who made enough money to buy the finer things, nice homes, fancy cars and every other material thing. He dated people with titles like M.D., Esq. and P.A., although he met them all via cyberspace and the relationships never lasted more than a few weeks. Even with his lackluster relationship record, he still brought in quality along with quantity.

"What does Will do?" I asked, suddenly interested in knowing more. What had I been doing wrong or, better yet, what was Will doing right in order to afford such lavishness?

"He's in the entertainment industry."

"Oh. So what exactly does he do?"

"Ask him when you meet him," Jarvis said.

We began to walk up the cobblestone pathway that led to the house. I was still in awe over how good Will had it. I tried to flush the amazement out of my system as we walked so that by the time I met Will, I wouldn't appear to be broke, ghetto and a foreigner to the high life.

The exterior of his house was an opulent combination of sophisticated architecture that offered lots of appeal. Cream, ivory and light beige bricks encompassed the large house. There were lots of windows, including two grand bay windows on each side of the large, stately looking, double-mahogany, antique wood doors complete with a wrought-iron doorknocker. I studied the house carefully as we stood at the front entrance, waiting to get in.

I expected to see a short, old, white-haired butler named Benson answer the door, wearing a black tuxedo and telling us to wait while he announced our arrival. Instead, a rather casual looking Will opened the door with a great, big smile, inviting us to come in.

Will was nothing like I had imagined. He was young looking, about twenty-seven to thirty years old, about 5'-7", medium-athletic build and very attractive. As I said hello and studied him the same way I had his home, a deeper look revealed that his honey-maple complexion had quite a few blemishes. I wondered why my overly critical best friend hadn't cut him off for not having smooth polished skin as he had done to men in the past, but then figured maybe Jarvis was maturing. Maybe Jarvis really did like Will and they had something that surpassed the acne. Besides, it was nothing a few trips to a dermatologist couldn't solve.

Will was casually dressed in baggy gray sweat pants, tan Timberland boots and a plain white T-shirt. I thought that maybe someone living in a house such as his would wear three-piece suits for leisure, but I then realized after seeing Will, even the high class needed downtime.

As we entered, there was music blasting. It instantly caught my attention as Will shut the door, gave Jarvis a hug, introduced himself with a firm handshake, then told us to follow him.

"Hey Jarvis, this is something new I've been working on. What do you think?" Will asked as he bobbed his head with an intense motion to the music playing in the atmosphere.

"This is hot. I like this," Jarvis said smiling.

"Really?" Will asked, sounding a bit surprised.

"Yeah, I do. Who is this singing?"

"You'll see. Jayson, what do you think?" Will asked.

"I'm really feeling it. This is your work?" I asked as we continued following Will. By then we were all moving our heads to the music.

"Some of it," Will replied with a faint laugh.

The voice singing to the track sounded as soothing as a light rain. It was as clear as buffed crystal, dynamic and grabbed hold of my attention making me feel the familiar lyrics. As I listened to the song and the way the singers voice teased my senses, gliding effortlessly on the track, going from high to low, hard to soft, it started sounding more recognizeable.

"Remember a little while back when I told you I might have some good news for you but I wasn't sure?" Jarvis quizzed

"Yes."

"Well here it is!"

"What do you mean?"

"You don't hear anything that sounds familiar?"

"Oh my God, that's you singing isn't it?"

"Yes, but that's not what I'm talking about dummy."

"What is it then?"

After just a few more seconds I finally realized why the lyrics sounded so familiar, they were my words. Jarvis had taken something that I'd written and arranged a melody for it. As I listened intently to the beautiful music, my first sincere piece of happiness in days flooded my soul. Speechless and in awe, I stood motionless and silent, unable to do anything but beam.

"So do you like it?" Will asked

"I love it!"

"I love it too. You have a real way with words which is why I want you to do some work for me. I have dozens of artists who are incapable of writing lyrics like these. I could really use talent like yours. That's if you want to," Will said still excited by the music.

"Before you answer that Jayson, Will works with people like your favorite singer in the whole wide world,

Faith Evans." Jarvis said imputing his two unneeded cents into the conversation.

"Of course I would like to write for you. Just tell me when, what, and where you need me to be and I'm on it!"

"Driven. I like that. You can do a lot with that kind of attitude... Jarvis told me about your book. Good luck. Hopefully you will find some time in between your soon to come author fame to write for me."

"I'm sure I will"

And in those few moments I'd found lost contentment. For a brief moment I was able to forget about my problems and let go of everything that had previously plagued me.

For the first time in my life I was validated and it felt great. Someone else thought I was talented which left me with a feeling of invincibility.

On our way home, I looked at my cell phone and noticed that Dorey had called me three times while I was at Will's house. My first instinct was to call him back and tell him about every wonderful second I had experienced that night. With him being the man I loved, I wanted to tell him so he could share in my accomplishment. He would have been almost as happy as I was to hear the good news, but I decided not to call. I would be following up with Mr. Pettis from the bank that next morning and wanted to hit Dorey with a double dose of good news that would be sure to blow him away. Besides, I knew he would mention his proposal.

I was ninety percent sure I was ready to say yes, but needed just a little more time to get the remaining ten percent together, so that my "Y*es*!" would be emphatic when it finally escaped my lips.

Therein that remaining ten percent were questions I wasn't sure I was ready to ask or know the answers to, questions for myself and questions for Dorey. I wanted to know if by marrying him did he mean with an actual ceremony, minister and wedding party. Did he mean just a commitment to be with me for the rest of his life or was it just a grandiose attempt at winning me back? Was I ready to marry a man, and even though I identified as a secure homosexual, was I ready to profess it to the world with a ring, vows and the promise of forever? The biggest question of all was of Dorey's intent. Was he really serious about the whole marriage thing or was it just a grand attempt at winning me back because I had been avoiding him.

I still needed more time to think. Thankfully Dorey had remained very patient as I was finding my answer.

22

Who would have known that just a little reassurance could do so much? Hearing something I had penned given new life in the way that the poem-turned-song had, actually sparked my creativity and ushered in works that were just short of incredible. For a moment I was able to put my money woes, daddy drama, and the Dorey dilemma aside just long enough to birth creativity.

Initially, when Jarvis took my words and arranged them, I wasn't sure if he was doing it as a handout or if he really liked my work. Either way, after that night at Wills house, I went on a rampage, writing every chance I got. I was sure that one of my pieces would one day leave its legacy and fulfill my dream of being a well-known author.

Soon, ever mounting anticipation took control of my life with the release of my first book just days away. The arduous tasks of final edits, promotion and legal matters left my head spinning. Though feeling especially exhausted as I prepared to relax after a long day with an even longer bath, I smiled, realizing that I wouldn't trade the current state of my life for anything.

Already Barton Publishing was inquiring about the second manuscript of my two-book deal with them. While brainstorming ideas, I found solace in my bathtub, full of hot, foamy liquid.

I heard the phone ringing in the background, but ignored it, taking a deep breath of air into my lungs. I then dipped my head back into the water as the night went on, debating if I wanted to do another book of poetry or start a work of fiction.

Suddenly, I was jolted out of my relaxed mood and my heart started racing. I heard a loud, violent beating on the bathroom door. Jarvis had left to go to the club about two hours ago, and no one else had a key to the apartment. I wondered if Jarvis had given Will a key, and if he had, what was so important that Will had to pound on the door that way?

"Who is it?" I yelled.

"It's me, Jarvis!"

"Hold on," I said reluctantly getting out of the tub, wrapping my body in a towel and unlocking the door.

"Wassup? I thought you were at the club?" I asked, figuring there had to be something wrong.

"I was at the club. Didn't you hear me calling you? I've called you, like, five times!" he said frantically.

"I heard the phone ringing, but I've been in the tub. What's going on?"

"I'm not really sure how to tell you this, but, well, do you remember Patrick?"

"Patrick?" I asked.

"Yeah, the boy that was with Dorey that night in the club when you first got back in town."

"Oh, yeah I remember him now. What about him?" I asked.

"Well, I saw him tonight in the club and he told me, he said…"

"What did he tell you?" I asked, sensing distress in Jarvis' words and I began to feel uneasy.

"He and a few of his friends, it was the news all over the club…they were talking about it..." he said in between long pauses.

"What! What were they talking about?" I demanded, no longer able to take him pussyfooting around his purpose.

"Dorey is dead," Jarvis said bluntly.

I felt my body go numb. It took about five minutes of me standing in complete silence for those words to register and allow me to formulate a response.

"What!" I demanded, not even sure that I wanted to hear those words repeated, but I had to be sure I'd heard him correctly.

"Everyone was talking about it at the club, and I called you as soon as I heard. Patrick was really a mess over it."

"How do you know it's true? You know how those club kids like to make up rumors. They're always saying someone has AIDS or is dying the minute they don't see you in the club for a while. *How do you know it's the truth*?" I asked as tears started to form in the wells of my eyes. One by one, large drops started to make a procession down the sides of my face.

I tried to convince myself the news wasn't real. Dorey was a big practical joker. I'd lost count of the times that he had pulled pranks on me. For all I knew this could be just a sick hoax. Though this kind of joke was far from funny, I prayed that there was no truth in it. My heart couldn't take it being reality. I wanted Jarvis to say *gotcha, just playing, April fools* or anything that would put my troubled mind at ease, but he offered no condolence.

"I'm sorry, but it's true," Jarvis said reluctantly.

"How do you know? *How do you know for sure he's dead*?"

"Because Patrick told me everything. He said that I could find Dorey's obituary in Thursday's paper, and I've been driving around to every store that was open, looking for a two-day-old paper. Anyway, I finally found one and…" he pulled out a section of newspaper from his back pocket and slowly handed it to me.

The paper was already opened and folded to the obituary page. I felt ill once my eyes zeroed in on the name that I silently prayed would not be there.

Surrounded by a sea of names and elaborate obituary ads with pictures and short life stories of the recently deceased, lurked the unwanted obituary of the love of my life. It was plain, offered little information and was very short in contrast to the others on the page.

Dorey Braxton
Age 25 of Atlanta, GA, passed away suddenly December 24, 2004, in his home.
He is survived by his children, mother and father. At the family's request, services will be held privately.

Those words bore holes in my heart one by one as I read Dorey's death announcement. With reading those tragic words came the sad realization that he was really dead. It was no joke. The short paragraph was very uninformative and left me with many unanswered questions. Dorey was young, too young, and had too much going for him. How did he die? The last time I'd seen him he'd appeared healthier than ever.

"Did Patrick say how he died?" I asked with uncontrollable tears still rolling down my face.

"They say he shot himself," Jarvis said softly and very apologetically, as if he'd been the triggerman.

"That's impossible!"

In my heart I knew that Dorey would never kill himself. Even though the obituary did give me proof that he was dead and I still tried to fight that fact, I just couldn't accept that he'd died by his own hand. But I scoured the paper at least fifty times, and it didn't give any information on the cause of death. Maybe there was a chance that it was true.

Remembering that the paper was two days old raised even more questions. Had I missed the funeral? Maybe it wasn't too late and the service hadn't been held, but even if it was, how would I know?

After all the years of knowing Dorey, it wasn't until that moment that I realized I wasn't that close to any of his family. The gay side of Dorey that he hid so well from the world left our love excluded from the public and kept me away from having normal relations with his loved ones. Though I'd met many of his family, I didn't have any of their numbers, nor did I know where they lived. I had to get in contact with someone who could let me know what was happening.

Maybe they were listed in the phone book. I raced into the living room, still not completely dried off from my bath. Frantically I searched the pages of the telephone directory for anyone with the last name of Braxton whose first name was familiar. I needed information, how Dorey died, where and when the funeral was being held.

Then I realized I did have one number of someone who could shed some light on the situation. It was a number I never in a million lifetimes imagined I would use under normal circumstances, but I was in despair and thus resorted to desperate measures.

I swallowed my pride, along with all the hatred I felt toward Shawnquetta, and frantically dashed past Jarvis to the phone, dialing her number as fast as I could. After just a few short rings, her voicemail came on. I left a message, pleading she call me as soon as she got the message.

After hanging up, I had this nagging suspicion that I was too late for Doreys's funeral. With Shawnquetta not answering the phone, I thought about the possibility that the funeral could be underway.

I knew the good fortune that had recently presented itself was too good to be true and without failing, nature's balancing act came around full circle, giving me sorrow to stabilize the joy I had experienced. Luckily, Jarvis had gone to the club that night. If not, I may not have found out about Dorey for weeks.

As I played with the platinum engagement band Dorey had given to me, I wanted to shoot myself because of the treatment I had been giving him. I never gave him my "yes" and had still been somewhat distant, wrapping myself up in everything but Dorey.

I began to hate myself for being so stupid, for being so petty, selfish, for every bad memory I held of him, and for avoiding him the way that I had. Dorey had been reaching out, showing up to the apartment and calling, but I ignored him and almost shut him out of my life while I put my own un-deserved happiness first, never realizing that he was the one who inspired me to write so much in the first place.

Maybe he had really needed to talk. If the rumors of him committing suicide were true, then maybe I could have done something to keep him alive. I could just imagine the pain Dorey had undergone with his family finding out he was gay and Shawnquetta threatening to keep his children from him.

I started to think of all the many reasons why Dorey died and felt that I could possibly be to blame for many of them. I told myself that I would never forgive myself for not being there for him. Maybe if I had been more available I would be making wedding arrangements instead of mourning.

The vision of Dorey proposing to me replayed in my mind constantly. The sweetness of his words played evil tricks with my head and the last few words he'd said to me started to stitch indeliblt onto my conscious, making me feel like I should be the one dead instead.

I felt like my mind was closing in on itself and sending me ever closer to insanity. Things had been going so well, but now I was right back to square one, a life spinning out of control. Why was the universe playing such an evil game with me?

The phone was still in my hand, but not for long. I catapulted it across the room, sending it flying toward the wall, where it crashed and broke into three pieces. I followed the phone to the wall and began abusing the plaster with my bare fists, beating it over and over until there were about a half a dozen holes and my hands were bloody and sore.

Jarvis tried to comfort me, grabbing me tightly, but it was pointless. I continued my violent, mild nervous breakdown, kicking things, breaking things, and trying to hurt myself until my body became exhausted and could do nothing but curl up into a ball in the fetal position on the living room floor, crying like a newborn.

"Hey, Jay, this is Shawnquetta. I see that you called. How are you doing," She said so sincerely, it made me question her sanity. She never worried about my wellbeing before. Why the sudden change?

"I'm doing ok under the circumstances."

"Yeah I know, I'm just trying to stay strong and keep it together for Jasmine and this pregnancy, you know?"

"Yeah. Did they have the funeral yet?"

"No, it's going to be on Wednesday at the Scottish Rite Cathedral at 11am."

"Oh ok."

"Jayson, before you hang up, I know that the two of us have had our fair share of issues, but I just want you to know that since Dorey has passed, its made me question a lot of things. I don't know what the two of you had, but. I do know that he loved you a lot and I was wrong for going about things the way I did. I want to apologize."

"That's real big of you Shawnquetta. So you said Wednesday at the Scottish Rite Cathedral," I asked completely avoiding her insincere apology.

"Yeah, I will see you on Wednesday. Keep your head up okay Jayson."

Unsure of why the usually selfish and self-absorbed Shawnquetta had made a 360° change, I paid her naught.

Whatever her motive, it was a safe assumption that it wasn't good. But at least I knew where and when the funeral was going to be.

23

I had passed by this same church many times, watching it from the highway and always wondered if it was as beautiful on the inside as it was outside. Today my questions about the grandeur of this large cathedral were answered. In fact, the view from the outside was almost no match to the even more captivating interior. Stained glass windows were everywhere, filling the inside of the chapel with hundreds of rainbow-like beams of light. From the pale, marble floors to the soaring cathedral ceilings high over my head, at first sight everything was beautiful.

And then there was the contrast of Dorey's coffin, surrounded by a ton of flowers and small crowd of sorrow-filled mourners. The church was huge, but the amount of people inside it was really insignificant in comparison. There were only about twenty people gathered there. I was so disappointed at the turnout, knowing that Dorey had many more people who loved him and would have shown up, had the funeral not been kept so private. It was only because of my relentless pursuit to find out all the information I could that I was able to be in attendance.

The air in the church felt almost too warm and thick to inhale as I walked somberly into the doors of the cathedral. Soon, Dorey's dark, wooden, open casket stole my attention from everything else. I wanted to look anywhere but at Dorey's corpse, but somehow couldn't take my eyes off of it. The vision of my ex-lover's lifeless body appeared to be that of a stranger as he lay settled against the white, satin material.

That was the first time I'd ever seen him dressed up in a suit, the first time I'd ever seen him with a messed up haircut, and the first time I'd seen him wearing makeup.

When my legs started to grow weak, making me feel like I couldn't walk any further and the room started to spin, I felt Jarvis' hand grabbing me hard on the back of my arm and guiding me to the nearest seat. He was right by my side serving as my strength. He had been my rock ever since I had found out about Dorey's death.

The only reason I had found the strength to make it out of the house that day was for the sake of paying my last respects. Riddled with guilt over the fact that I may have played a major role in Dorey's departure had my subconscious attacking me to the point that those around me feared for my life. I hadn't eaten and I slept very little. Nightmares plagued me and disturbed my rest. While awake, I was barely responsive to my environment.

Shawnquetta was crying so hard that her mascara was streaming down her face, leaving a trail of smoky black liquid. Jasmine was still too young to realize the seriousness of what was going on. She just sat there silently crying, alternating stares between her sobbing mother and dead father.

Chills started to race through my body as soon as a tall, heavy-set, chocolate brown woman with a towering gold hat began to sing. The first few words to her rendition of "Precious Lord" belted out in her strong and husky alto danced off the walls of the church so powerfully and with so much emotion, that by the time she had got to the line "I'm tired, I'm weak, and I'm worn," I had to bow my head in my lap, trying to disappear. Even though I was out of view from most in the back of the church, I didn't want to risk anyone seeing me crying and in such distress. As she continued to sing, I felt as though the words couldn't have described the pain I was feeling any better if I had written them myself.

When the lady in the gold hat finished singing, there wasn't a dry eye in the church. I wiped the tears from my eyes and looked up to see even Jarvis shedding a few tears. Then, the music was replaced by the painful sounds of weeping echoes all around.

After a few moments, the preacher, who was a short, gray-haired man with obvious signs of time full on his face, stood up to the microphone and began reading the eulogy. The first few paragraphs sounded eerily familiar to the first conversation that Dorey and I ever had. It was filled with a short story about Dorey's childhood growing up in Georgia and a quick timeline filled with all of the many accomplishments he had attained during his short life. Hearing those words brought a smile to my face as I was reminded of that first day back at Clark Atlanta when we met. I wished I could go back in time and re-do everything; I would erase anything that would have possibly led to Dorey's death.

After the eulogy, the preacher went into a slightly more emotional and unrehearsed dialogue about the type of person Dorey was. He also stressed over and over how sad he was that Dorey had to die so young. My questions were answered in the eulogy after the pastor talked about the complications he experienced from his leukemia. If I wasn't sure of anything else, I knew the man I had loved for so long could never have taken his own life.

Dorey seemed so healthy and had been doing so well. Why had things gone so terribly wrong so fast and without admonition?

As all the people in the crowd cosigned with the preacher's dynamic words, saying their "amens" and "that's rights" after almost line, Jarvis and I looked at each other with puzzled expressions. The man the preacher was describing was nothing like the Dorey I had known. By the way the people agreed with the preacher's every word, I had to assume that Dorey must have had a second personality that he kept hidden whenever he was around me, only revealing the second secret side to his family and the other to me and his friends. The Dorey Braxton the pastor and everyone else in the church seemed to know was definitely not the same man with whom I was in love.

Dorey was not the quiet man the preacher described. He loved life, loved to laugh and his spirit was far from reserved as the preacher announced. As the preacher describeed a beautiful love shared between Dorey and Shawnquetta and the mourners said 'amen' I knew they were all delusional, because Dorey couldn't stand her.

After the fire-filled preacher was done with his inspirational words, the gloomy mood from earlier was replaced with a more lighthearted one. However that lighthearted mood quickly evaporated after just a few short moments when it came time for the final viewing.

I just couldn't do it. As the choir started to sing "I'll Fly Away" and the mourners slowly passed the coffin, I couldn't force myself to move from my seat. I didn't have the strength to get any closer to the disturbing scene at the altar. I wanted to hold on to the memories I had of Dorey when he was actually living and breathing, not lying in a coffin.

As Shawnquetta passed by the casket she brought all of her drama down the isle with her. Waterworks, sobs, moans, and shrieks, accompanied as she staggered slowly to see Dorey. She threw up her hands and paused for a few moments yelling out mumbled words before receiving an escort from two pallbearers on each side of her arm. Her Oscar worthy act didn't stop there, next when she made her way to the body, she threw herself down on top of Dorey hugging and kissing him screaming out '*NO!*'. She should have been screaming out '*IM SORRY*' for all the hell she'd put him through in his last days. But I guessed her actions were her way of showing her supposed "undying love".

I just assumed that Shawnquetta had outted Dorey like she promised and told his family about me in the process. I didn't want to get up there in front of the family and have them cause a scene in church after finding out I was their dead loved one's gay ex-boyfriend. That would have sent me over the edge for sure. Even if they hadn't known about me, I felt much more comfortable staying seated in the back.

"Oh *bitch* please. Get a grip!" Jarvis said just loud enough to catch the attention of some of the congregation as Shawnquetta continued making an ass of herself.

The choir continued singing as representatives from the funeral home started to close Dorey's casket. As I realized that this was the last time I would ever get to see his beautiful face, the atmosphere in the church suddenly grew too close again.

In the silence I heard the voice of God resounding over the voice of my pain.

"Just how long has it been since you were in my house?"

"It's been..."

"It's been too long."

"You're still running from me and though I continually try to give you the love you've searched for in everyone but me, you always run away."

"We used to be so close. What have I done to make you turn away?"

"It's not you, it's me."

"That night when you fought your father I was there to save you, and the night you tried to kill yourself I was the one that spared you. I kept you safe through heartaches, tragedies and blessed you with undeserved success. I kept you alive because I have work for you still. But you cannot keep making promises which you have no intention of keeping. I know your heart and I know what you are capable of. All I ask is that you give me a second chance as I've given unto you. I want you to give me the attention you've been wasting on those who don't deserve it. Do that and you will see what great things your life has in store. Just stop running."

Atlanta's hot afternoon sun shined brightly hitting me with its intense heated beams as soon as I came to. I had passed out, and when I awoke I was surrounded by a crowd of people with worry and concern on their faces. The great effort I had made to go unnoticed at the funeral was in vain. Just moments before, when Jarvis and I were leaving the church, I'd lost control. The world around me faded to black, and I felt myself falling.

Did I just have a religious experience, or was it just a dream while I was blacking out? I wondered. Whatever it was felt as real as anything else I'd ever experienced. There was a peace that found me as a looked around concentrating on the words I heard while in my trance-like state. That day was the first time I heard the voice of the Most High. The words He whispered never left my mind. They were powerful, true and enough to spark much-needed modifications. I knew it was time for a change in my life and there was no better time than the present.

"Wait here. I'll bring the car around," Jarvis said, still watching me attentively to make sure I was okay.

"Okay," I said, fanning myself with Dorey's obituary, trying to stay cool while baking in the hot sun in my black suit.

The sight of the long, silver hearse parked out front made me feel faint again. It was giving me the creeps. In fact, just about everything that had to do with the funeral that day gave me the creeps. Death and I never really interacted well with each other. Even after all of the many relatives that had passed away in my life and attending many funerals, I still got this weird feeling every time I was in the presence of a dead body or anything that had to do with death. Though I knew death was as natural as life itself, it still gave me the heebie-jeebies.

As soon as Jarvis pulled the car up to where I was standing, I got in quickly. Looking back at the church, I noticed that the doors were now being held open by ushers at each side, as six pallbearers slowly carried Dorey's casket outside.

We sat there in the car, listening to commercials playing softly on the radio until they placed the coffin into the hearse, and then we drove away.

Jarvis kept a watchful eye on me in between glances at the road, making sure I was okay. He drove with one hand on the steering wheel and the other on my shoulder for consoling. All I could think about was how my life needed a change and promised myself that this time I really would make a conscious effort to make those alterations. Dorey's passing showed me that life was fleeting, and I didn't want to die a mess.

Just then, the commercials on the radio ended and the deejay's voice came on strong through the airways, announcing that he had a new song that was sure to be a hit.

"This new song right here, I just want to make it known. It's hot like fire and you're hearing it first on Atlanta's number one station for hip-hop and R&B KJZ 97.5FM so get ready. From her new album coming later this summer, here she is the beautiful, the talented, Ms. Faith Evans with 'This song.'"

After a few moments, I finally processed what was happening. This was *my* song. A song that I had written was being played on one of the best-known stations in the country.

The universe was continuing to play its game. Here it was, one of the saddest days of my life. Yet as fate would have it, the same day I had to say my final goodbye to the love of my life, something that should have been overwhelmingly joyful was happening.

I'd always dreamed about the day that something I had written would be recognized as great. There it was, the day I had longed for and through the sadness of everything, I couldn't get excited.

"Please tell me that you are happy," Jarvis said.

"Happy? How could I be happy?" I asked.

"How often does something like this happen? I know you're sad about Dorey and that's understandable. But in life, you have to celebrate your victories and grow from defeat. I will not let you mope right now. This is a huge accomplishment that most people will never get. Your book is finally out *and* you have a song playing on the radio as we speak. Years from now do you want to tell people when you heard your first song on the radio you were sad about it? *No!* This is a once in a lifetime thing. You will never again get to hear your *first* work being played, so cheer the hell up," he demanded.

Even if I allowed myself to be happy that my life's biggest accomplishments to date was taking place, the sad irony was that it was a tragic ending of one chapter in my life and what would mark the beautiful beginning of another all in one day. I still felt like I was riding life's broken seesaw. Every time I was at the top, some twist of fate would drop its heavy load, sending me right back down to a sad starting point.

Why couldn't I have everything, my first song on the radio, my book and Dorey there to share it with?

While the song played I smiled and at the same time I cried, still full of mixed emotions. I remembered the promise I had made to Dorey years ago about being a big writer one day and couldn't believe it was coming true. Even though he wasn't living to see it, share in my accomplishments, or give me the satisfaction of saying "I told you so," I still knew he saw everything, wherever he was, and he was proud.

24

"Dorey, I feel like its been forever since I've been by to see you, and since we haven't talked in so long, there is so much that I have to share.

"First, let me start by saying that I am still very much in love with you and probably always will be. Nothing has changed, that much you should already know.

"My every intent was to come by much more often, but things have really started to turn around for me lately, making it hard to see you as much as I want.

"The books are doing extremely well. The first as you know was the book of poetry you inspired me to write, and the second just released. I dedicated it to you because our relationship was the basis. We had so many highs and lows that I had to right a book about it.

"Dr. Kline. has been like an angel in disguise. She's really been pushing for my success and her contacts have led to marketing strategies and success that Barton wouldn't even be able to contemplate. I never imagined seeing success like this when you inspired me to put the first book together. Thank you again for giving me that push that was greatly needed, I owe everything to you.

"Aside from the books, I've also gained some credibility in other areas of writing. Will still has me working on projects for his artists, and through his connections, I've been making a name for myself in the entertainment industry. It seems like I'm constantly getting calls to write songs for people. And no matter how many times it happens, every time I hear one of my songs being played on the radio or see something I've written on the billboard charts, the feeling gets better each time.

"Baby, I'm finally doing something that I love and getting paid very well to do it.

"The ongoing saga with my family is getting better. It's been a constant struggle, but I think our relationship just might work. We just recently got back from Cancun. Honestly, most of the time cultivating conversations with my father was like fighting a losing battle, but I can still see that he is really trying. We all go to counseling sessions about once a month, and so far I can already see a difference. My parents are coming around to the point of acceptance and I'm almost at the place of forgiveness.

"One thing I'm so grateful that you've taught me is that if you love someone, show it and don't let anything stand in the way of giving that love your all because you never know when that person may not be around. I truly love my parents, I may not fully understand them, but I love them, so I'm going to do all I can to make our relationship work. I just wish I would have learned that lesson about love before you died. Who knows maybe we would have gotten to say our vows before you went and died on me.

"But enough about me and my issues... You know everybody misses you so much. Jasmine has grown up so fast. She is the female version of you, only prettier. And she seems even happier now that your mom has custody of her. She's doing a great job of raising her, much better than that low down Shawnquetta ever could.

"I know you probably know by now, but I was shocked when I heard the news. Shawnquetta has always been trifling, but her lying about being pregnant with your child was just crazy. I should have been smart enough wonder how she could have known she was pregnant so soon after having sex with you. I should have questioned her validity right from the start.

"People started getting a little suspicious a few months after your funeral, and Shawnquetta's stomach never started showing any signs of growth. Around month number six she made up a lie about having a miscarriage due to stress, only to find out later, through one of her big mouth friends, she was never even pregnant to begin with. Nobody's seen or heard from her, but trust me your family has been looking. I think she may have moved out of state after all that drama, but wherever she is I hope she stays there.

"Oh yeah, speaking of missing persons. Remember that dude Red I told you about? Well, I still haven't seen hide nor hair of him either. The good thing is the damage from his brief presence in my life didn't last. I'm still HIV negative and I was able to get all of our money back. I know the money never really mattered to you but just know that we got it back and there is a whole lot more where that came from. With my success and the large insurance policy you left behind. Now money troubles are a thing of the past.

"I will make sure that your family is always taken care of, especially your daughter because I know that's what you would have wanted. Most of all, I will make sure no one ever forgets about how incredible you WERE.

"Rest in peace baby. I love you."

Dorey O. Braxton
1979-2004

348925

Made in the USA